Preface

Forestry practice has become the standard textbook for forestry students and forest and woodland growers, owners, managers and planners in Great Britain. It was first published in 1933 and this is now the 11th edition. Much of the basic information provided in the previous edition only five years ago remains unchanged in this publication. However, there have been considerable changes and advances in forestry practice since 1986 and this edition encompasses these. In particular, the task of planning for second rotation plantations is becoming a major issue in British forestry and a new chapter is devoted to this subject, drawing on extensive experience in one of Britain's major upland forests.

Forestry practice is often referred to as Bulletin 14 which has been the Forestry Commission's series number for the title since 1933. A new family of technical publications has recently been introduced which places the 'Bulletin' series in a special category for supplying technical information to forest managers. The wider audience is now addressed by means of the popular 'Handbook' series which has a livelier form of presentation and which is freely illustrated.

Forestry practice now takes its place in the new Handbook series where it will stand alongside similar publications such as *Urban forestry practice* and *Farm woodland practice*. While every effort has been made to ensure that *Forestry practice* will meet fully the high standards of presentation expected of a Forestry Commission Handbook, sight has not been lost of the need to keep the cover price within the reach of students.

Contents

Forestry Practice

Forstwirtschaftliche Praxis

Summary

This Handbook presents an account of current forestry practice in Britain, with advice on planning and management for growers, owners, planners and students. The sequence of operations from plant propagation to final felling and restocking is dealt with comprehensively. Environmental issues are taken into account and the reader is offered guidance on wildlife management, landscape design and recreation planning.

Zusammenfassung

Dieses Handbuch bietet eine Beschreibung der gegenwärtige forstwirtschaftliche praxis in Grossbritannien, mit Rat über Planung und Betriebsführung für Züchter, Waldbesitzer, Projektemacher und Studenten. Die Arbeitsfolge von Pflanzenvermehrung bis Abtriebsschlag und Wiederaufforstung wird ausführlich beschrieben. Umweltsfragen werden in Betracht gezogen, und Orientierung über Tierweltbewirtschaftung, Landschaftsanordnung und Erholungsplanung wird dem Leser angeboten.

La Pratique Forestière

Résumé

Ce Manuel présente un exposé de la pratique forestières actuelles en Grande-Bretagne, avec des avis sur la planification et la gestion pour les cultivateurs, les propriétaires de forêt, les planificateurs et les étudiants. On décrit de façon complète la série des opérations de la propagation des plantes jusqu'à la coupe definitive et le reboisement. On tient compte des questions de l'environnement, et on présente aussi des conseils sur la gestion de la faune, le dessin des paysages et la planification de la récréation.

1 Forestry in Britain

Introduction

The purpose of this Handbook is to describe the elements of good silviculture in British conditions. The term 'silviculture' is used in the widest sense embracing all aspects of the cultivation of trees both as a crop and for the many other purposes woodlands serve. Past editions of *Forestry practice*, known to many as Forestry Commission Bulletin 14, tended to confine forestry practices to those suited to afforestation of bare land. This was not surprising since such work has been at the heart of British forestry development during the present century with its primary aim of substantially increasing our forest estate to create a reserve of timber.

This revision of *Forestry practice*, while still covering the principles and practice of afforestation, is enlarged to include the range of forestry operations and situations likely to be encountered in the many different kinds of forest and woodland we have. This introductory chapter seeks to place in context British forestry, silvicultural systems used, and the opportunities and constraints prevailing in the last decade of this century.

Forestry in Britain

At the present time Britain's forest cover amounts to about 10% of our land surface: an area of 2.2 million hectares. This is more than twice the area recorded at the beginning of this century when the forest cover reached historically its lowest proportion, just under 5%. Nevertheless, the better position today still compares unfavourably with other European coun-

Table 1.1

Percentage of Forestry cover			
Country	Percent	Country	Percent
Portugal	40	Norway	27
Spain	31	Sweden	64
W.Germany	30	Finland	76
France	27	USA	29
Italy	23	Canada	38
Bel./Lux.	21	USSR	42
Greece	20	Japan	67
Denmark	12	World	31
U.K.	10		
Netherlands	9		
Ireland	5		
EEC countries	25		

source : Forestry Facts & Figures 1988/9

tries (Table 1.1) and is substantially below the estimate of 30% forest cover for the world as a whole; though it must be noted that the latter percentage includes both closed and open forest formations, e.g. savanna woodland.

Only a few countries have seen steady expansion of forest area during the present century and many, particularly in the tropics, have seen rapid diminution. Very broadly, forest clearance and forest creation are in balance in temperate countries while in the tropics the ratio is 10 to 1, i.e. 10 times as much forest is cleared as is regenerated and perpetuated. While not of direct relevance to Britain's forest estate, clearly what is happening elsewhere in the world must impinge on how our forest strategy and policy evolve.

The initiative leading to this record of steady expansion of British forestry was the decision in

J. Evans, *Chief Research Officer (South)*

1919 to establish the Forestry Commission, both to encourage private investment and to create new forests on behalf of the state. In previous centuries, and indeed dating back to the epoch-making publication of John Evelyn in 1664, encouragement of afforestation and rehabilitation of the nation's woods had been given from time to time, but it was the devastation during the First World War of what meagre resources remained that was largely responsible for precipitating decisive action. For its first 35 years, the Forestry Commission's main objective was to create new forest to build a strategic reserve of timber; necessarily this resulted in plantation establishment mostly on open hill land of poor agricultural quality. This challenge led to much of the research and plantation practice for which Britain is now internationally famous. Since the Second World War policies have evolved mainly to accommodate ever widening objectives as the value of forestry as an economic resource, recreational facility and important contributor to the landscape and wildlife environment came more and more to the fore.

Forest types

The types of forest found in Britain can be classified in many ways but it is helpful to group them by their origin and by their composition. Both categories are shown below and should not be seen as mutually exclusive.

Semi-natural woodlands

No woodlands in Britain have been wholly devoid of man's direct influence at some stage since medieval times. There are no truly natural woodlands. There are, however, probably some 300 000 ha of semi-natural woodlands where the degree of intervention

Today, Britain's forests and woodlands supply about 12% of our total wood and timber requirement. When the recently established forests come into full production this percentage is expected to rise to over 20%. Current policy is aimed at continued expansion of the forest estate carried out sensitively and in association with all the multiplicity of demands on land in our small, heavily populated island. At the present time the expansion of tree planting on to good quality farmland, often with broadleaved trees, represents the first major departure from concentration of effort on relatively poor upland areas. Paralleling this trend is the increasing use of trees to rehabilitate industrial waste ground and the development of urban and community forests. Also, there is renewed interest in bringing back into sound management neglected, usually broadleaved, woodlands, many of which were once coppiced but are no longer suited to management in this way. For these reasons it is important that the practising forester acquires and applies skills which go beyond those needed when British forestry was dominated by the upland afforestation period.

has been low or intermittent, or where coppice has been worked in the past. In these, the present woodland composition, mostly derived from natural regeneration, begins to approximate what might have arisen naturally in terms of species and, probably to a lesser extent, age class structure. Most such woodlands consist of native broadleaved species though some 12 000 ha of native Scots pine are found in the highlands of Scotland.

Many semi-natural woodlands are present on sites

Native Scots pine woodlands in Glen Affric.

Coppice woodland in West Sussex.

which are believed to have always been wooded. Where firm evidence shows a site to have been under woodland from before 1600 such woodland is called '*ancient* semi-natural woodland'. It is probably the nearest forest type we have to the 'wilde wood', which covered much of Europe in pre-Bronze Age times. There are many examples of recent semi-natural woodlands where owing to abandonment of land or restriction of grazing, new woodland has arisen by natural means.

Plantations

As the name implies these are forests established by planting trees. It is the method whereby the great bulk of Britain's forest expansion has been carried

out during this century. However, it is clear, even in such 'natural looking' forests as the oak dominated parts of the New Forest and Forest of Dean, that tree planting, particularly in Napoleonic times and the years immediately following, was widely practised. Also much of the upland woodlands and shelterbelts of beech and Scots pine were planted during the eighteenth and nineteenth centuries.

Coppices

These are broadleaved woodlands created by recruiting the stool shoots arising from cut stumps as the next tree crop. In past centuries more than half of all woodlands were managed in this way to yield the multiplicity of small roundwood products, tan bark

4

and fuel that were the mainstays of rural life and pre-coal energy needs. Sweet chestnut in south-east England is the main coppice crop today, though rehabilitation of some hazel and mixed broadleaved coppices is increasing for reasons of wildlife, game, firewood, charcoal and rural crafts.

Monocultures and mixtures

Another way of classifying forest types is by their species composition. Where only one species is present or largely dominates, such forest is called monoculture. The great majority of Britain's new plantations are grown as monoculture for reasons of efficiency and productivity; it is logical to grow only the best species suited to the site. Many broadleaved woodlands are established as mixtures of two or three species for silvicultural and economic reasons. Most semi-natural woodlands contain half a dozen or more tree species, but by no means invariably so, as the Caledonian Scots pine and western sessile oak woods show.

Another aspect of species composition is the use of native or introduced (exotic) ones. Forestry expansion this century has relied on the latter since increasing our softwood resource was the main objective and none of Britain's three native conifers was well suited to or capable of fast growth on most impoverished upland soils. The nation's Victorian arboreta had shown that species such as Sitka spruce, Douglas fir and lodgepole pine grew consistently well and these north-west American conifers have come to form the mainstay of our productive forest estate along with Japanese larch, Corsican pine and Norway spruce. Almost all broadleaved woodland consists of native or long naturalised species, sweet chestnut and sycamore falling into this latter category. The role of exotic broadleaves such as red oak and southern beech, though promising, is likely to remain very minor.

Age class structure

Forest stands can also differ in the tree age classes present. Plantations are established in a single year, or a narrow band of years where failures have to be replaced, and are essentially even-aged. Stands raised from natural regeneration may contain trees varying in age from a few to many years difference depending on the silvicultural system and, in a very few exceptional cases, may contain young, immature and old trees all together. This very uneven-aged or all-aged character typical of selection systems of management is rare. Also it does not necessarily equate with naturalness. It is now clear that much of the 'wilde wood' that formerly covered Europe was not the forester's supposed 'ideal' of a mixture of all species of all ages intermingled, but a mosaic of patchy even-agedness.

Open woodlands

By no means all timber trees are grown in closed forest. Hedgerow trees are an important source of hardwood timber and, in the past, many park-like 'woodland' areas – the wood pastures and chases of medieval England – were managed for both grazing (mainly deer) and tree growing. Today, apart from experimental work with agroforestry, growing trees in an open environment is primarily for amenity reasons. Apart from points of detail, good forestry practices apply equally to the cultivation of such trees as to those in forest stands.

Silviculture in existing woodlands

Thinning

After the establishment phase, thinning is the most powerful tool the forester possesses to manipulate development of the stand and the quality and quantity of final crop trees produced. Thinning practice in

Britain initially followed the conservative principles employed in France and Germany but has become increasingly intensive to match closely removals from a stand with its growth capabilities. This has led to the concept of thinning at marginal intensity so that over the life of the crop the maximum amount of timber is removed in thinnings without significantly impairing overall yield of wood from a site. This point is stressed because thinning practice elsewhere in the world has developed in largely subjective ways. In British plantations the consequence of this thinning policy maximises efficient growth of trees. In most conifer stands the importance of individual tree selection becomes secondary to removal of the right quantity of trees over time.

By contrast, in broadleaved stands, while thinning intensity is important and has as powerful effect on stand development as for conifers, the much poorer stem quality of broadleaved trees requires far greater attention being paid to selection thinnings to favour the best stems. Though an over simplification, it can be said that conifer thinning is mainly a question of intensity; broadleaved thinning a question of proper tree selection.

In upland forests where exposure levels are high and soils shallow, conventional thinning is severely restricted or not carried out at all. The breaking of the canopy which thinning causes, renders such relatively unstable stands liable to much greater risk from windthrow.

Clear felling and replanting

The principal silvicultural system used in Britain for both broadleaves and conifers is clear felling and replanting. Clear felling all trees at the end of a rotation is the most efficient method of harvesting, and replanting ensures successful restocking of the ground provided due care is taken. Where investment has been made in creating a plantation forest resource, as is the case in Britain over the last 70 years, maximising the returns from that investment is clearly prudent.

Secondary reasons for adopting this silvicultural system are to provide opportunity to restock the ground with a different species or a better seed origin and because most of our principal conifer species are unreliable for natural regeneration. Although all species set some seed, both the timing and the quantity are unpredictable.

It is recognised that clear felling is the most abrupt intervention in the life of a forest that can happen and particular attention is placed on the landscape consequences.

Group regeneration

Because of the disadvantages of clear felling from an amenity point of view, in many lowland forests, especially of broadleaves, openings are made in the stand to begin the regeneration process without its wholesale removal. Many silvicultural permutations exist but regeneration by groups is the most common. The opening or gap, of perhaps 0.1 or 0.2 ha, may be restocked naturally from seed from the adjacent trees or by planting. Several openings are made across the stand to yield a reasonable quantity of timber and further ones created every 5 years or so until the whole stand is cut and regenerated over 20 or 30 years.

Such silvicultural systems which retain an element of cover on the site bring several benefits in terms of wildlife, landscaping and general attractiveness: the penalty is increased costs of working, both in harvesting and protection of restocking.

Natural regeneration

Natural regeneration is not a silvicultural system in its own right but one of the possible operations to achieve satisfactory restocking of the ground once a stand has reached maturity. In Britain all native broadleaved species set seed though, in the case of oak and beech, at relatively long intervals between heavy mast years. If this is recognised, and due preparation given, most broadleaved stands are capable of being regenerated in this way provided proper attention is given to ground conditions and adequate protection from browsing. The question of a 'free' successor crop in this way must be set against the need to time fellings and regeneration operations with the occurrence of a good seed year (and not the demands of the timber market), the need to enrich gaps in the restocking and the need to weed, respace and clean the young crop as it develops.

With coniferous species natural regeneration is much less certain, with the exception of Scots pine, both because conditions for setting seed for the exotic species appear less favourable and because in most cases stands are felled before biological maturity when seed production is at a maximum. Nevertheless, in some instances, e.g. Sitka spruce in many parts of Wales, restocking by natural regeneration is feasible.

As a silvicultural system natural regeneration provides no opportunity to improve the genetic quality of the stands beyond that of selection within the developing crop. Nevertheless, since 1985, as a system of restocking woodland natural regeneration has been actively encouraged through grant aid for broadleaved woodlands.

Coppice and coppice with standards

Coppicing is largely confined to sweet chestnut (in south-east England), hazel and some mixed species coppices in the lowlands: a far cry from when more than half of lowland woods were managed in this way. Nevertheless, it is clear that even long neglected coppices can be reworked (with the exception of hazel older than 40 years), and a steady yield of small roundwood products provided. Coppice, especially where standard trees are retained, is a visually attractive system of management with many wildlife benefits.

Constraints and priorities

In discussing the main features of silviculture in forest stands, reference has been made to constraints such as windthrow risk and operational costs. Also it is increasingly clear that all forestry operations are subject to public scrutiny and the differing requirements of wildlife conservation, enjoyment of forests, and the appearance of our countryside, will come to influence more and more the conduct and skill of those involved in forestry operations. Though perceived as constraints in terms of maximising profit from growing trees, such influences are good opportunities for foresters to show their skill in managing a resource valued for many different purposes. This gradual trend to greater involvement and wider debate in decision making is to be welcomed by foresters as custodians of one-tenth of Britain's land.

Forest establishment

Natural colonisation

Almost anywhere in Britain, if land is protected from browsing and grazing it will become stocked with a woody crop in a relatively short time. Below 300 m altitude the net result of such natural colonisation will often be reasonable stands of oak, ash, sycamore and, in places, beech. Of course, the stocking of such trees may be incomplete and usually a mixture of several species including less commercially valuable forest trees will be present. However, the widespread distribution of deer, rabbits and hares and the presence of livestock on much farmland has precluded this natural process in most cases.

Afforestation in the Dyfi valley.

However, where these browsing and grazing pressures are very low or eliminated, for example on old quarry sites, roadside and railway embankments and some open heathland, woodland has been added to the total forest cover. Indeed, this gradual accretion partly explains the statistic that the total area of broadleaved woodlands between 1947 and 1980 remained largely unchanged despite the conversion to conifers of many broadleaved woods in the 1950s and early 1960s period.

Afforestation by planting

Creation of new forest by planting has been emphasised already as the principal tool by which Britain's forest estate was increased. This is likely to continue to be the case.

During the phase of upland afforestation the three main silvicultural challenges were choice of species for our cool, temperate climate and poor soils, how to improve soil aeration and weed suppression at the planting site, and overcoming nutritional deficiencies. During the course of 40 years' experience, from the 1920s to the 1960s, these three challenges resolved into the widespread, but not exclusive, use of Sitka spruce, ploughing as the principal site preparation technique, and the application of phosphate fertiliser on many upland soils at the time of planting. These three factors largely explain the relatively high average yield class (11) achieved on what were once seen as inhospitable, unproductive sites. Refinements in establishment practice, improvement in ensuring greater stand stability, and improved genetic material, will continue to improve productivity, but the creation of a major forest resource on poor land has been well demonstrated.

In the lowlands, up until the recent expansion of interest in planting on farmland (of which 80% is of broadleaved species), the bulk of afforestation concerned acid heaths such as the Breckland in East Anglia, and at Cannock and in Dorset. While establishment on such sites proved relatively straightforward, the incidence of frost and the restriction of species to pines were major constraints on forestry potential.

British and European silviculture

The predominance of plantation forestry, based largely on exotic species, is in marked contrast to countries such as France, Germany and Scandinavia. Their much larger areas of natural forest and long history of high forest management have led to silvicultural practices employing long rotations and natural regeneration. Relatively little investment has been needed to create forest but, interestingly, the advantage Britain has reaped from building a plantation resource of carefully selected species, is an average productivity two to four times greater than most other European countries.

Afforestation during this century has so far been mainly in the uplands.

9

2   Seed

The choice of seed source is one of the most important decisions faced by the forest manager. An error in judgement can lead to crops with poor stem and branch form or prone to pests and diseases. Within the genetic constitution of the seed is the potential for either good or poor tree growth, and since even small increases in growth rate or improved timber quality can lead to a much enhanced return on investment, the advantages of using the best available seed from which to grow the planting stock are considerable.

The production of trees with good vigour, health, stem form and crown habit depends upon two interacting factors, the genetic constitution of the seed and the environment in which it is planted. The forest manager must do his utmost to ensure that the seed he uses is of superior genetic quality for his purposes and that it is planted in the environment to which it is best suited. These considerations and the regulations governing the sale and purchase of seed are the main subjects of this chapter. Forestry Commission Bulletin 59 *Seed manual for ornamental trees and shrubs* and Bulletin 83 *Seed manual for commercial forestry species* provide detailed information on the more specialised aspects of collection, storage, processing, testing, dormancy and pretreatment. Table 2.1 summarises most of the important information on seed production for the more widely used forest species.

Seed sources

Provenance and origin

Tree species which occur over wide geographic areas develop sub-populations with slightly different characteristics which may, for example, be related to altitude and day length. These populations are usually not physically distinguishable from one another but each one is just a little better suited to its own particular environment. Seed from these populations (or ecotypes as they are called) is usually better adapted to grow in a similar environment to that in which its ancestors grew. In order to realise a tree's maximum potential growth it is clearly wise to plant seedlings on a site to which they are best suited

Counting seed for germination test.

11

P.G. Gosling, Head of Plant Production Branch

A germination test in the laboratory.

and this is why information on the seed source is so important. The place from which a seed lot has been collected is called the *provenance*. The *origin* is where the most remote traceable ancestors came from.

Seed orchards

The Forestry Commission and some private estate owners have established seed orchards in which trees are exclusively managed for seed production. They are composed of individuals selected from parents with highly desirable attributes grown either by grafting or by raising seed derived from controlled parental crosses. They are called respectively 'clonal' or 'seedling' seed orchards. Seed obtained from an orchard is more likely to be superior in genetic quality for timber production than that from plantation or natural sources.

Seed stands

Early in their rotation, young conifer stands selected for their good quality or perhaps rare origin are heavily thinned to keep only the best trees for seed production. Depending upon species and tree quality, these may be entered into the National Register of Seed Stands. Seed collected from a local registered seed stand, where the origin is known to suit the planting environment, is the next best source after orchard material. But if locally produced seed is unavailable, or even the best local stands are of inferior quality, then seed collected from a high quality source growing on a broadly similar site elsewhere in Britain is a good alternative. When imported seed is the only source available caution must be exercised and, if there is a choice, an origin known to produce trees which will grow well in the region to be planted should be used.

Table 2.1   Seed production of trees in Britain

Common name	Age of first good seed crop (years)	Age of maximum production (years)	Average interval† between good seed crops (years)	Recommended time of seed collection‡			Notes
				Earliest	*Normal*	*Latest*	
Broadleaves							
Ash*	25–30	40–60	3–5	Aug.(1)	Oct.(2)	Nov.	(1) For immediate sowing (2) For stratification for 16–18 months
Beech**	50–60	80–200	5–10	Sept.	Oct.	Nov.	Flowers sometimes damaged by late frosts
Birch*	15	20–50	1–2	Aug.	Aug./ Sept.	Sept.	Good seed producers in Britain. Some seed most years, though sometimes empty
Chestnut, horse**	20	30	1–2	Sept.	Oct.	Nov.	
Chestnut, sweet**	30–40	50	1–4	Oct.	Oct.	Nov.	A warm late summer is required to ripen nuts. Collect biggest nuts only
Oak,** sessile and pedunculate	40–50	80–120	3–5	Sept.	Oct.	Nov.	
Sycamore	25–30	40–60	2–3	Sept.	Sept./ Oct.	Oct.	Some seed most years
Wych elm**	30–40	40	1–2	May	June	June	

13

Table 2.1 Seed production of trees in Britain (*continued*)

Common name	Age of first good seed crop (years)	Age of maximum production (years)	Average interval† between good seed crops (years)	Recommended time of seed collection‡			Notes	Notes on seed collection	Average number of cones per hectolitre	Average yield in grams of clean seed per litre of cones
				Earliest	*Normal*	*Latest*				
Conifers										
Scots pine	15–20	60–100	2–3	Nov.	Jan.	Feb.	Some seed borne every year	Some seed retained in cones until early spring	5500	6
Corsican pine	25–30	60–90	3–5	Nov.	Dec.	Jan.	Most seed produced in SE & E England		2800	9
Lodgepole pine	15–20	30–40	2–3	Mid-Aug.	Late Aug./ early Sept.	Late Sept.			4500	4
European larch	15–20	40–60	3–5	Nov.	Feb./ March	April	Flowers often damaged by frost	As for Scots pine	10 000	10
Japanese and hybrid larch*	15–20	40–60	3–5	Sept.	Sept.	Nov.	Flowers often damaged by frost	Also during November in Scotland in some years. Collect before European	9500	14
Douglas fir	30–35	50–60	4–6	Sept.	Sept.	Oct.		Collect when cones a light golden brown or yellow colour	3000	5

Table 2.1 Seed production of trees in Britain (*continued*)

Common name	Age of first good seed crop (years)	Age of maximum production (years)	Average interval† between good seed crops (years)	Recommended time of seed collection‡ Earliest	Normal	Latest	Notes	Notes on seed collection	Average number of cones per hectolitre	Average yield in grams of clean seed per litre of cones
Conifers (continued)										
Norway spruce	30–35	50–60	—	Oct.	Oct.	Nov.	Rarely seeds heavily	As for Scots pine	1000	13
Sitka spruce	30–35	40–50	3–5	Sept.	Sept./ Oct.	Dec.			3600	9
Grand fir	40–45	—	3–5	Aug.	Aug./ Sept.	Sept.	A poor seed producer	Collect immediately the scales loosen and the cone softens, otherwise seed will be lost	700	26
Noble fir	30–35	40–60	2–4	Aug.	Aug./ Sept.	Sept.			2200	22
Western hemlock	30–35	40–60	3	Aug.	Sept.	Sept.		Collect as soon as cones colour from bright green to yellow and the tips of the seed wings are visible and a light brown colour	58 000	13
Western red cedar	20–25	40–60	2–3	Aug.	Sept.	Sept.	A good seed producer		190 000	14
Lawson cypress	20–25	40–60	2–3	Aug.	Sept.	Sept.	A good seed producer		107 000	44

Notes: † The figures refer to the intervals between good seed years. In Scots pine, for example, 2–3 years of relatively poor production will generally follow a good seed year. ‡ Sept./Oct. means at the end of September or beginning of October. *Collect by special felling. **Collect fallen seed from the ground.

National Register of Seed and Plant Sources

Since 1973 the Forest Reproductive Material (FRM) regulations, which arise from our membership of the European Community, have required the Forestry Commission to maintain a National Register of seed stands, seed orchards and poplar stool beds. These sources must have been inspected and found to meet certain criteria. Under the regulations this register is required only to cover the following 13 species and one genus:

European silver fir	Weymouth pine
European larch	Douglas fir
Japanese larch	beech
Norway spruce	sessile oak
Sitka spruce	pedunculate oak
Austrian and Corsican pine	red oak
Scots pine	poplar

An owner wishing to have registered a plantation of one of the listed species or a poplar stool bed should contact his nearest Conservator of Forests for advice. An inspection fee is charged whether or not the stand meets the criteria prescribed by law.

Regulations governing the sale and purchase of seed

Under the FRM regulations, seed of the 13 species listed may not be marketed within the European Community unless from a source approved and registered by the Forestry Commission in Great Britain or by the relevant authority in another member state of the European Community or Northern Ireland. (Exceptions are seed or cones to be used in tests for scientific or non-forestry purposes under the written authority of the Forestry Commission.) Seed of European Community species originating from outside European Community countries must have been specially authorised for marketing in Britain by the Forestry Commission and furthermore, seed of the 13 species from wherever it originated, may only be marketed if it has been tested at an Official Seed Testing Station during the same seed testing year (1 July – 30 June) as that in which it is marketed. Seeds of European Community species intended for export to non-EC countries are not covered by the FRM regulations; however they may be covered by alternative similar regulations of the importing country.

For species not covered by the FRM regulations, seed from recommended sources is still to be preferred to seed from 'unknown' sources but only the normal consumer legislation protects the purchaser.

3 Nursery practice

The raising of young trees in nurseries is the first stage in planting a forest and the Forestry Commission has had long experience of this work backed by years of research. Over the years the subject has been fully covered in Forestry Commission Bulletin 43 *Nursery practice** which is currently under revision. Anyone concerned with the management of forest nurseries is advised to consult that publication.

Precision sowing.

Objectives

The principal objective of the forest nursery is to produce good quality plants in uniform batches as cheaply as possible. In this context, good quality can be taken as meaning a sturdy plant with a well balanced root and shoot and with a well developed root system.

Method

Plants of the required standard are usually raised by a two-stage process. Seed given the appropriate presowing treatment (chilling where dormant, etc.) is sown on prepared seedbeds designed to ensure maximum germination of the seed and good growth of the seedlings in their first growing season. The seedlings are then lifted when dormant and transplanted into lines where they have enough space to grow into well shaped plants fit to go into the forest at the end of the growing season, referred to as '1+1

Netting seedbeds to prevent damage from birds.

17

D.R. Williamson, Silviculture (South) Branch, and **W.L. Mason**, Silviculture (North) Branch

transplants'. This is the basis of the process but there are modifications. Less favoured nurseries or slower growing species may not produce usable plants in 2 years and longer periods may have to be allowed in seedbeds and lines.

Nursery soils

Both seedlings and transplants of conifers and most broadleaved species (there are exceptions, e.g. ash and poplar) grow best in acid soils. Soils in the range pH 4.5 to 5.5 are the most suitable for forest nurseries. pH levels below 4.5 are too acid and those above 5.5 are too alkaline. Soil texture is also important because nursery work involves soil cultivation in winter and early spring. At these seasons, soils with a clay plus silt content exceeding 15% are often too wet to cultivate, a factor which delays the nursery operation so that valuable growing time is lost. Although the clay or silt fraction in soil is valuable for its water and nutrient retaining characteristics the factor of 'workability' is more important in the nursery and the nutrient retention problem is overcome by the addition of fertilisers. The best nursery soils therefore are the sandy loams or even sands which have the additional merit that they tend to be sufficiently acid.

Seedbeds

Successful seedling production depends on a number of factors of which the two most important (provided good quality seed is available) are usually correct preparation of the seedbed and time of sowing. A properly prepared seedbed with a good tilth, well consolidated, is essential. If sowing is delayed beyond the optimum date (normally March in the south and April in the north) the time available for growth in the summer will be reduced and may result in seedlings too small to transplant. Sowing density is also important and depends on the species being sown and the viability of the seed. A seed lot which has a high proportion of viable seeds has to be sown at lower density to give adequate growing space to the seedlings, the normal aim being to produce 600 usable seedlings per square metre.

Transplants

Correct spacing is important to allow plants to develop to the required size, but the success and cost of transplanting are very dependent on the workability of the soil. Light sandy soils are both easy to work and quicker to dry out in the spring. Lining-out is generally carried out using machines that place seedlings in position and firm the soil round the roots. The seedlings are fed into the planting mechanism by hand. The machines most widely used produce 5 or 6 rows of transplants with a density of 100–150 plants per square metre. Careful plant handling is essential for ensuring good survival after transplanting.

Plant nutrition

Successful nursery production depends very much on correct fertiliser application for both seedbeds and transplant lines. Suitable fertiliser machines have been developed from many years research, and experience has shown how local knowledge, soil analysis and foliage analysis can be used to modify the general recommendations to suit a particular nursery. Most nutritional regimes are based on the use of both organic and inorganic fertilisers although the inorganic material supplies the major part of the crop's nutritional requirement. Organic fertilisers are used mainly because they help to maintain soil organic matter levels, thus preventing deterioration

Sequence of operations in the sowing beds, from left to right
  i. Tractor and rotavator preparing seedbed;
 ii. Precision sower sowing seed;
iii. Gritting the seedbed.

Close-up of side-cutting operation.

in moisture holding capacity and workability. Results of experiments suggest that inorganic fertilisers alone will give satisfactory results over long periods of time and while soil organic matter levels have fallen, there has been little evidence of a fall in productivity. However, some soils, particularly heavy soils, have tended to become markedly more difficult to cultivate after continuous inorganic fertiliser application.

Weed control

An effective weed control programme in the forest nursery is vital because weeds can compete with and damage tree crops, especially at the seedling stage. Hand weeding is expensive. Its effect is short lived and manual removal of weeds can damage small seedlings. Therefore weed control using chemical

herbicides has been generally adopted throughout the forest nursery industry.

Diphenamid is used as a standard pre-emergence spray on seed beds of all species except birch and alder. Simazine is still widely used for weed control in transplant lines but other herbicides are being introduced particularly where nurseries have problems with weed populations which have become resistant to triazine herbicides.

Herbicides should be selected according to the weeds present. Before using any herbicide it is essential to read the product label. This carries full instructions regarding application rate, timing and the protection of the operator and the environment. The subject is covered in Forestry Commission Occasional Paper 22 *Forest nursery herbicides*.

Irrigation

Most nurseries can expect a dry spell at some stage in the growing season. Lack of available soil moisture can reduce germination and survival of seedlings and limit growth of transplants. In addition, many herbicides and granular fertilisers require moist soil to be fully effective. For these reasons a good irrigation system is an important tool in nursery management.

Nursery protection

It is normal practice to net seedbeds for about 12 weeks after sowing to prevent birds taking seeds and small seedlings. Nurseries should be fenced against the risk of damage from rabbits, stock and deer where necessary. Damage from fungi, insects and climatic factors (e.g. frost) will occur in most years and the nurseryman needs to be able to diagnose the problem and take appropriate remedial action. Further details can be found in Chapter 6.

Close-up of under-cutter. (Wrenching bar.)

OTHER PLANT PRODUCTION TECHNIQUES

There are a number of alternative techniques to the main nursery method of seedbed and transplant lines outlined above. They are:

Use of containers

The majority of tree seedlings produced in this country are grown in open ground nurseries. However, approximately 8–10 million seedlings are produced in containers each year and this represents about 7% of the total annual production. Most container seedlings have traditionally been conifer species such as Corsican pine. More recently there has been interest in producing broadleaves in containers. At least ten British nurseries are now offering containerised tree seedlings in their catalogues.

Unlike bare-root nurseries, container nurseries are not confined to sites with a suitable soil type. There is a lowered risk of a build-up of soil problems such as weeds, diseases and insect problems in container production. However, a high capital investment is required for facilities such as polythene tunnels, compost mixers and filling machines, irrigation and liquid feed systems, etc.

One of the main advantages claimed for container seedlings is reduced transplanting shock because roots are not damaged. Claims about superior survival of container plants compared with bare-root transplants are often based on anecdotal evidence. Experiments have provided little evidence to show that containerised plants are superior to good quality bare-root planting stock. It seems unlikely that container-ised seedlings will replace bare-root plants for standard forest use in the UK. Container plants offer advantages for small-scale planting by inexperienced customers, in situations where there may be some delay between receipt and planting, and for out of season planting. Containers also have logistical advantages for nurseries, since the time between sowing and selling is reduced.

Seedbed cloches

Improved germination and first season growth of pines can be obtained by covering seedbeds immediately after sowing with clear polythene tunnel cloches. In northern nurseries, this technique can make the difference between being able to produce a transplantable seedling in one year and having to hold seedlings over for a second growing season. To prevent seed competition it is advisable to sterilise seedbeds where cloches will be used. Sowing density should be reduced (compared with normal seedbeds) to ensure seedlings do not become spindly. Cloches are removed 12–16 weeks after sowing and thereafter normal nursery methods apply.

Undercutting

Instead of transplanting seedlings their roots can be severed in the seedbed by drawing a sharpened steel blade through the bed at the appropriate depth. The effect of this is to cut the main root and stimulate the formation of a branched and fibrous root system. Seed has to be sown at a lower density to give greater growing space and this involves controlling weeds over a larger area of seedbed and into a second season of growth.

However, undercutting has the important advantage of eliminating the costly transplanting operation. The technique of precision sowing and undercutting has been successfully applied in New Zealand for large-scale pine production. Trials have been carried out in this country (at Wykeham Nursery) to develop a successful precision sowing and undercutting regime for a number of conifer species. Undercut plants generally are sturdier and have a more favourable shoot to root ratio than non-undercut transplants. Undercut stocks also appear capable of withstanding cold storage better than transplants. In forest experiments, undercut plants generally show as good a survival rate as transplants and in Douglas fir, performance is markedly better.

Vegetative propagation

Traditionally, few forest trees have been grown from cuttings with the exception of poplar, willow, London plane and elm and among the conifers Lawson cypress, Leyland cypress and western red cedar. However, recent research shows that cuttings of a range of coniferous and broadleaved species can be propagated successfully from stem cuttings provided that these are collected from young (less than 4 years old) parent trees. Cuttings are raised under an intermittent mist irrigation regime in a polythene greenhouse. Species successfully propagated under such conditions include sessile oak, gean, lodgepole pine, Sitka spruce and hybrid larch. This technique is of particular interest where highly productive material can be identified that is too scarce to allow use of conventional nursery techniques. The use of rooted cuttings of superior Sitka spruce for field planting in upland Britain is now firmly established (see Chapter 4).

Lifting first generation Sitka spruce cuttings in a polyhouse.

Cold storage

A cold store is an essential facility in modern nursery management. A small store can be used to hold seedlings temporarily before transplanting should weather or soil conditions prove unfavourable. Similarly, a larger store may be used to hold lifted transplants in a dormant state until forest planting conditions are suitable. Several types of cold store are available and handling and packaging systems must be adapted to the particular store used.

Trends in nursery management

During the last 20 years, the trend has been to concentrate production in larger nurseries where skilled labour and management, specialised equipment and favourable site conditions can be brought to bear on a large output and so result in lower production costs.

4 Tree Improvement

Introduction

Tree improvement begins once species choice has been made. The tree breeder now has the opportunity of selecting and breeding within the species to improve the various adaptive and economic characteristics considered important for the development of that species thereby increasing the profitability of forests. Examples of characteristics (traits) that can be included in breeding programmes are vigour, timber quality, stem and branch quality and disease resistance.

Successful tree improvement depends on the amount of variation available within the trait and to what degree this variation is heritable, i.e. is controlled by genetics and can be transferred from one generation to the next.

The aim of this chapter is to identify the source of natural variation, show how that variation can be exploited by the tree breeder using breeding strategies (programmes), give an idea of the likely genetic gains, and outline possible future areas of development. Examples mainly cite Sitka spruce since it is Britain's most extensively planted timber species.

Sources of variation

The bulk of variation exhibited within a species occurs at two levels:

1. provenance/origin;
2. within provenance.

The potential gains available by selecting within each of these two levels is considerable.

Provenance/origin

Most of the species we plant commercially in Britain occur naturally (in either Britain or abroad) over a very wide area. The different *native* locations from which seed are collected are referred to as *origins* (often called ecotypes or races). *Provenance* is the name given to the place in which the stand of trees is growing. Thus, if seed is collected from a stand of Sitka spruce growing in Kielder Forest, but the seed which gave us that stand was imported direct from Queen Charlotte Islands (QCI), then the *provenance* is Kielder and the *origin* is QCI.

It is probably not surprising that parcels of seed collected across the range of a species with an extensive distribution such as the 1800 mile north/south distribution of Sitka spruce, will behave in quite a varied manner when they are all planted on the same site in Britain. Plants of Alaskan origin, from the very northern end of the Sitka spruce distribution are used to long day-lengths during the growing season and cease growing in Britain around the end of July. This results in a short growing season and therefore generally poor growth rates. Plants of Californian origin, from the southern end of the distribution, are adapted to growing on until the day-length is quite short. In Britain this means they continue to grow until late November/early December. Therefore, although southern origins have a much longer growing season than northern origins, they are more susceptible to autumnal frosts.

Extensive field experiments planted around the country on a range of sites have shown that the most suitable Sitka spruce origin for the bulk of Britain is from the Queen Charlotte Islands (QCI), an origin

S.J. Lee, Tree Improvement Branch

Demonstration lines of trees from across the natural distribution of Sitka spruce. The trees increase in height on going from the left (Alaska) to the right (North Oregon).

mid-way between the two extremes; with a latitude similar to the Borders area of England and Scotland (see Figure 4.1). This origin combines acceptable growth rate with low probability of frost damage. However, if trees are to be grown on a site not prone to early autumnal frosts (e.g. most of Wales, southwest England, extreme west coast of Scotland), then seed origins from Washington and northern Oregon can be used and will grow at a faster rate than QCI. For example QCI Sitka spruce planted on a mid-elevation site in Wales may grow at Yield Class 14 (see Chapter 11, 'Management for timber production') whereas Washington Sitka spruce on the same site would be expected to grow at Yield Class 16 or better. Conversely in a very exposed area, or one subject to early autumnal frosts, an origin from north of QCI may be better adapted resulting in a more commercially viable crop. The correct choice of origin therefore can make a major difference in the value of the crop. As a general rule risks should not be taken. An origin which will produce an acceptable crop with a high degree of probability is better than a potentially higher-yielding one but with much less certainty.

Origin can affect more than just growth rate; stem form, stem density, foliage colour, wood density, insect resistance and many other traits can also vary across origins.

Lodgepole pine, for example, is a species with an extensive east/west as well as north/south distribu-

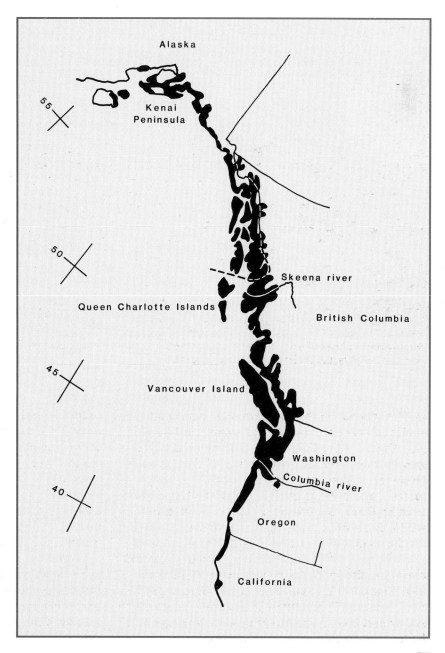

Alaska

55

Kenai
Peninsula

50

Skeena river

Queen Charlotte Islands

British Columbia

45

Vancouver Island

Washington

Columbia river

40

Oregon

California

FIGURE 4.1   Natural range of
Sitka spruce, *Picea sitchensis*
(Bong.) Carr.

tion. The variation for vigour, stem form, and susceptibility to basal bow across the origins of this species is considerable and great care must be taken over the choice depending on site details and prospective end use, e.g. the bushy, slow growing Alaskan origins are suitable for Christmas tree production or as a nurse with Sitka spruce on deep peat sites, whereas the faster growing Skeena River origins still exhibit acceptable form and are more suitable for pure commercial crops on mineral sites (see Figure 4.2).

This subject is fully covered in Forestry Commission Bulletin 66 *Choice of seed origins for the main forest species in Britain.*

Improvement within a provenance

Once the most suitable seed origins are known there remains scope for substantial improvement within those origins by selecting good quality stands and superior individual trees. The distribution of the total variation between and within origins varies by species and trait; but most economic traits such as vigour exhibit approximately 60% variation within and 40% between origins. The potential for selection and breeding within the *provenance* (if the stand of trees is growing in Britain) is therefore clearly high.

At this stage, however, the genetic gains are more hard-won involving expensive, long-term breeding programmes. Such programmes have been in operation for a number of species in Britain; in some cases for over 40 years. This point again demonstrates the importance of origin selection. If Sitka spruce of QCI origin were planted on mid-elevation sites in Wales it could be a further 20 years before the Yield Class is increased from 14 to 16 through selection and breeding. A similar increase achieved now by simply planting stock of a more southerly origin is clearly a cheaper option; substantial improvements within the most suitable origins can follow.

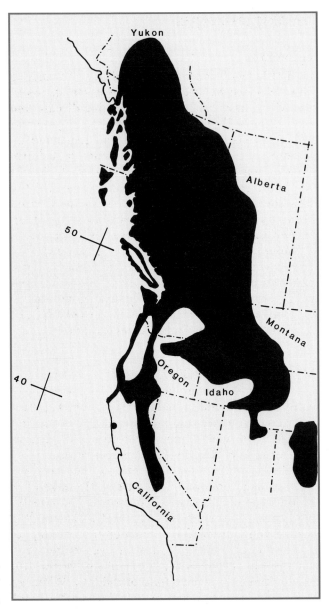

FIGURE 4.2 Natural range of lodgepole pine, *Pinus contorta* Douglas ex Loud.

28

Breeding strategies

Seed stands

The first level of improvement within a provenance is the selection of seed stands. These are stands of trees which have been selected as being disease free and having well above average quality, vigour and form. Such stands are inspected and registered by the Forestry Commission in accordance with European Commission Directives. (See Chapter 2, 'Seed'.)

If planting stock from a seed stand is to be used the first choice would be to obtain seed of the desired species and provenance from a registered seed stand from within Britain, as close as possible to the area to be planted. Failing that, seed should be purchased from a registered seed stand elsewhere in the European Community (EC). If no seed of the desired provenance and species is available from within the EC, seed may be purchased from outwith the EC. (Consult the Forestry Commission for details.)

Improvement at the individual tree level

The next level of improvement involves selection of highly superior individuals or 'plus' trees, testing their genetic quality, and bringing them together in a seed orchard where they inter-breed to produce superior quality seed for forest regeneration.

The appearance of an individual or trait we see in the forest is a combination of the genetic make-up of the tree, the environment it is growing in, and the interaction between these two effects. The result of this combination of effects is called the *phenotype.*

The environment often has an over-riding effect and the phenotype is a poor indicator of the true genetic make-up or *genotype* of the tree. When we look at a superior phenotype it is impossible to tell with confidence if it really is a good genotype, whether it has benefited from a favourable environ-

A large, well established Sitka spruce progeny test site.

ment, or if there has been an interaction between genotype and environment. The only way to find out the actual genetic quality of the tree is to carry out a progeny test. In its simplest form this involves collecting wind-pollinated seed from superior trees selected from all over Britain and growing these progeny along with a standard control (reference datum point such as improved direct import material) on a number of very uniform sites. If the phenotype truly is of superior quality it will pass an element of that superiority on to the next generation. In such tests, progeny can be compared with each other and the standard control. The progeny, therefore, are used to give an indication of the genetic quality of the selected tree. It is then possible to impose selection standards amongst the families in the test with regard to vigour, form, or any other relevant traits.

The standards of selection used in Britain are very high ensuring only the best genotypes enter the breeding population. Only the top 10% of tested genotypes are found acceptable across a range of sites; the other 90% are discarded.

Since different traits express themselves at different stages in the life of the crop, progeny testing can be a long-term process. For example, it is not currently possible to assess wood density of Sitka spruce with acceptable accuracy until the trees are approximately 15 years old. Correlations with data collected earlier than 15 years have thus far proved unreliable. Vigour, however, can be accurately assessed after 6 years due to good correlations with 15 year (and older) data.

It is therefore around 20 years after 'plus' tree selection before seed orchards can be established based on the results from progeny tests.

Seed orchards

Seed orchards provide the end product of a breeding programme. Orchards are managed for seed not timber. They are located in areas of the country which are conducive to male and female flower production and are free from pollen contamination by the same or hybridising species.

Seed orchards may be referred to as *clonal* if the various component genotypes are derived from grafts or *seedling* if the breeding trees are raised from seed. In the case of a clonal orchard, scions are taken from the mother tree which has been progeny tested; in seedling orchards the seeds will either have been collected from the mother tree in the forest at the same time as seed was collected for progeny testing or will be the result of controlled pollination between selected individuals.

Any seed orchards established following the procedures described above are known as *approved* seed orchards. An *untested* seed orchard is one established before any progeny testing is carried out. Seed from an untested orchard will be of poorer quality than that from an approved orchard since some of the trees selected in the forest, and present in the orchard, will be of poor genotype. Untested orchards should, however, give seed of better quality

Measuring an outstanding 6-year-old family in a Sitka spruce progeny test. Forty trees represent each family at each of three (minimum) sites. Family performance is the mean of all 40 trees at each site and is used as an indication of the genetic quality of the mother ('plus') tree.

for adaptability, vigour, and form than a seed stand, due to greater selection of the preferred phenotypes. Poor genotypes can be removed (rogued) from the orchard following progeny test results. A third category of seed orchard is *tested* seed orchard. These are orchard following progeny test results. A third category of seed orchard is *tested* seed orchard. These are control and has been found to be of high value.

Further details are available from Forestry Commission Bulletin 54 *Seed orchards**.

Hybrids and mutation breeding

A source of variation important in plant breeding for agricultural use is that caused by man. This may take the form of artificial hybrids or mutations induced following for example exposure to radiation. There are some well documented success stories of production of artificial hybrids, particularly in the horticultural world, e.g. Leyland cypress as a result of hybridising Nootka cypress and Monterey cypress.

In commercial forestry the practice of inducing variation artificially is less common than in agriculture since the amount of natural variation already available to the tree breeder is vast in most cases. Generating hybrids or mutations is a hit and miss approach. It is equally possible for example that a hybrid may exhibit the least desirable traits from each species instead of the most desirable. Hybrids are often costly to produce, involving controlled pollinations and possibly vegetative propagation, so their production is usually restricted to high value crops. There are notable exceptions. The most famous in European forestry is the hybrid between European and Japanese larch which combines the good form of the European with the good vigour of the Japanese, and is more resistant to canker as well.

Variation induced through radiation is not used commercially in forestry but is employed in agriculture.

Controlled pollination for vegetative propagation. Female flowers are isolated in plastic tubes well before they are receptive to pollen. Once the female flowers become receptive, a mixture of pollen from 10–15 superior quality males is sprayed into the tube. The small quantity of seed obtained can be multiplied up using vegetative propagation techniques.

Advanced breeding

Having obtained a breeding population of superior genotypes the programme can be developed by repeated crossing between those genotypes and selection within the resulting families. Various different mating designs exist; all have the same aim of increasing the frequency of desired genes within the genotype. Assuming selection is in a positive direction, the genotypes selected within each generation will be better than the last for the various traits considered economically important (usually vigour and form) whilst at the same time retaining a wide genetic base with good adaptation. The main considerations now become the various biological limitations of the species and costs of further improvement in relation to the return.

Active tree improvement programmes involving selection of superior phenotypes, progeny testing and seed orchard establishment exist for:

Sitka spruce   lodgepole pine   hybrid larch
Scots pine   Corsican pine

Amongst the hardwood species, some limited work was started in the past on:

beech   *Nothofagus*   alder   oak

More intensive breeding work is now commencing on oak, ash and sycamore. The status of the breeding efforts and availability of improved seed by species is given in Tables 4.1 and 4.2 respectively.

Vegetative propagation

It can take about 10 years following establishment, for a clonal seed orchard of the main coniferous species planted in Britain to yield commercial quantities of seed. During this period, new seed orchards will be planted based on the most up-to-date progeny test results. Each year the quality of the data and information available improves as more genotypes are evaluated.

Vegetative propagation can be used as a tool for shortening the time taken to realise genetic gain. Controlled pollinations can be carried out in seed orchards between superior female trees and a mixture of pollen from 10–15 superior quality males. This in effect simulates a seed orchard except that the best quality pollens available in that particular year can be used in the operation rather than limiting pollination to the more varied quality of the whole range of genotypes present in the orchard, as would happen following natural wind-pollinations.

The small quantity of seed thus obtained can be multiplied-up using vegetative propagation techniques. Improved genetic material obtained by this method is now commercially available for Sitka spruce.

Trees raised by this method will be more expensive than the collection of wind-pollinated seed and raising of seedlings, but the costs can be justified as the increased revenue from realising genetic gain earlier considerably exceeds the extra initial expenditure.

Genetic gains

Due to the poor indication of the value of the genotype from measuring the phenotype, gains at the seed stand level are small but still worthwhile. The more heritable the trait, the greater the gain for a given amount of variability. Thus, as a result of seed stand selection, quality traits such as form, which are often found to be more heritable than vigour, result in greater gains. Gains from seed stands are likely to be 2% for volume growth and slightly more for form, at rotation age. Also, since seed stands have already shown themselves to be well adapted to the site, mortality through poor site adaptation is likely to be less than when using unimproved direct import planting stock.

Table 4.1 Status of breeding efforts by main species and provenance (where applicable). Situation as of August 1989

Sitka spruce

1. General breeding population (QCI)

Well established programme.
Selection of 2000 'plus' trees now complete.
Most 'plus' trees now undergoing progeny tests.
32 hectares of approved seed orchards established (not yet in production).
Crossing to continue between tested genotypes.
Vegetatively propagated material available.

2. Southern breeding population (Washington/Oregon)

400 'plus' trees currently selected. Selection continues.
A small number of superior genotypes already identified.
One approved seed orchard established (not yet in production).

Scots pine

Well established programme.
Selection of 1000 'plus' trees now complete.
Most 'plus' trees currently being tested using progeny tests.
> 12 hectares of approved seed orchards established.

Lodgepole pine

Control pollinations amongst selected individuals both within and between a large number of different provenances.
Seedling seed orchards set-up in parellel to progeny tests.

Corsican pine

Selection of 1000 'plus' trees now complete.
Progenies of all 'plus' trees now established.
6 hectares of approved clonal seed orchards established (not yet in production).

Hybrid larch

800 'plus' trees of either European or Japanese larch already selected.
Selection continues.
Small number of progeny tests out in the field.
20 hectares of mixed European and Japanese larch untested clonal seed orchards established (not yet in production).

Table 4.2 Availability of improved seed (August 1989)

This is intended as a guide to the prospective purchaser of planting stock as to the various genetic qualities of stock that is potentially available on the market for the species in question.

Stock category

Species	1	2	3	4	5	6	7	8	(9)
Increasing genetic gain →									
1. Species for which breeding programmes exist									
Sitka spruce (QCI)			√				√	√	
Sitka spruce (Washington/Oregon)	√	√	√						
Sitka spruce (Alaska)	√								
Scots pine				√		√	√		
Lodgepole pine			√	√		√			
Corsican pine				√					
Hybrid larch			√						
Poplar									√

2. Species for which there is no breeding programme, but which are covered by EC regulations.

Species	1	2	3
European larch	√	√	√
Japanese larch	√	√	√
Norway spruce	√	√	√
Douglas fir	√	√	√
Beech	√	√	√
Sessile oak	√	√	√
Pendunculate oak	√	√	√
Red oak	√	√	√
Weymouth pine	√	√	
European silver fir	√	√	

All other species are not a part of either a breeding programme or EC regulations. There is therefore no restriction on collection or sale of seed but in some cases good quality stands of the species may have been inspected by the Forestry Commission and recorded as superior. In all cases if material is not available from such stands, seed should be collected from the best quality local source available.

Key to availability of seed in increasing genetic quality:

Stock categories:

1 – Import from most suitable origin outside of EC.
2 – Registered seed stands (rest of EC).
3 – Registered seed stands (Britain).
4 – Untested clonal orchards (unrogued).
5 – Untested clonal orchards (rogued).
6 – Approved seedling seed orchards.
7 – Approved clonal seed orchards.
8 – Vegetatively propagated material.
(9) – Clones from registered stool beds – poplar only.

For example with Sitka spruce, the most genetically superior QCI planting stock available (see below) is 8 – Vegetatively propagated material; the next best is 7 – Approved clonal seed orchard; the third choice would be 3 – Registered seed stands (Britain).

No progeny tests (of sufficient experimental size) have reached rotation age in Britain, so gains for end of rotation yields have to be predicted. However, there are indications that a 10% improvement in height at 10 years old is equivalent to a similar improvement in volume production per unit area at 30 years. A large number of other progeny test data have also shown that families expressing superior vigour at 10 years old are still outstanding at 15 and 20 years old. There is, therefore, no reason to assume that families identified around 10 years old will only grow fast early in the rotation; the indications are that increased yield is sustained.

A 10% increase in volume means that a site which would have grown Yield Class (YC) 14 if planted within unimproved material would now grow at nearly YC 16 (Forestry Commission Booklet 48 *Yield models for forest management*). Genetic gains in terms of height growth at 10 years old, from current-ly commercially available vegetatively propagated Sitka spruce, is around 15%. Figure 4.3 shows the

34

Clonal line at Ledmore, Central Scotland. All these trees are genetically identical having been raised by cuttings from the same stock plant. Note the uniformity in diameter.

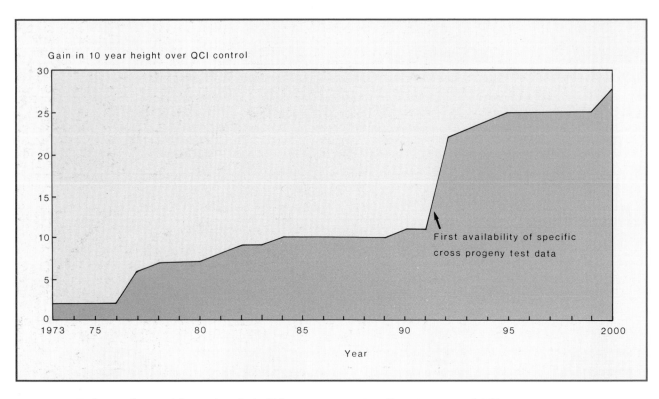

Gain in 10 year height over QCI control

First availability of specific cross progeny test data

Year

FIGURE 4.3   Pathway of potential genetic gain in Sitka spruce over time (from Mason and Gill, 1986).

likely increase in genetic gain into the early 1990s as the results from the first specific cross progeny tests become available (see 'Future developments').

In addition, but somewhat harder to quantify, is the expected increase in utilisable volume as a result of selected genotypes of improved form (stem straightness and branch quality). A further trait which is also the subject of selection and breeding within Sitka spruce is wood quality; gains for this trait have still to be quantified as this requires information on wood density from older crops.

Use of genetically improved crops may also decrease establishment costs. For example, weeding costs would be expected to decrease with fewer weedings required as a result of stock with more rapid early height growth.

It must be emphasised that none of the above gains can be realised unless sound silviculture is also practised. The use of genetically improved material is no substitute for good silviculture as outlined in the rest of this Handbook. For example, poor drainage which causes waterlogging, resulting in growth check of an unimproved crop, will do exactly the same to the genetically improved stock; however the losses will be greater due to the extra expenditure on improved material.

Micropropagation of Sitka spruce. Multiplication rates of 100 000+ are possible within one year.

SELECTION OF SUPERIOR OAK

Oak is the most important broadleaved tree in British forestry, covering approximately 30% of the broadleaved forest area, with a standing volume of *c.*30 million cubic metres in woodlands and a further 8 million cubic metres as hedgerow trees. However, few attempts have been made to improve the genetic quality of new oak plantations and the value of the final crop depends on the use of empirically derived silvicultural practices which may be time-consuming and expensive. Although recent legislation has ensured that seed for new planting stock comes from registered stands, these are approved on the basis of current appearance, which may result from an unknown silvicultural history rather than an inherent genetic superiority. The high value of good oak timber makes the introduction of superior genotypes with more reliable quality very desirable.

If vegetative propagation of superior individuals is to be used for a programme of clonal forestry the quality of the genotypes that are used must be assured. The principal aim of current research work is to develop a method to verify the quality of a genotype.

Mature trees with good and bad characters are being selected and cloned. These will be used in experiments to discover what features of growth and development are important in determining good and bad characters within the tree. At present the interest is in epicormic branches, stem form, and the distribution of crown biomass. These are probably interrelated phenomena associated with bud formation, bud development, branch growth and branch abscission. Detailed information on any of these topics is scarce and research is being concentrated on bud development during growth. Results from experiments will not only provide a better understanding of plant growth but also form the basis for development of a selection test that will enable identification of superior genotypes at the juvenile stage when propagation is easy.

Propagation techniques require further development for commercial use. Genetic variation in oak is great and the probability of selecting better provenances and superior individuals is high and, as little attempt has previously been made to improve oak, initial gains are likely to be large.

CALEDONIAN PINE

Scotland's relict native pinewoods form what is perhaps the most characteristic and ecologically important type of semi-natural vegetation still in existence in the country. Recent years have seen a re-awakening of interest on the part of foresters, conservationists, and landowners in preserving and managing these special tree communities. New measures to restore and protect the remnants of the Forest of Caledon are now under way.

The Forestry Commission's Northern Research Station near Edinburgh has investigated the measure of genetic resource still existing in these remnants, and what is the relationship (or the genetic similarity) between the pinewoods in different parts of the country. It was not sufficient merely to consider recognisable external features of the trees: the morphology of plants is notoriously variable, being greatly influenced by the environment. Instead, those characteristics of the tree which truly reflect its genotype were studied by an analysis of gene-products which are not susceptible to external influences.

This is the first attempt to characterise the natural variation in our only important native conifer, using objective genetic criteria. The results have been used to construct a 'family tree', or hierarchy, of all the sites, showing the degree of similarity or difference between them.

It is likely that most of the present-day pinewoods derived from European continental sources at the end of the last Glacial Period, but it is possible that two special western groups may have originated from small 'refugia' which were somehow able to survive the glaciation, later to recolonise the restricted areas where they are now found. If this is the case, there are in Scotland two distinct races of Scots pine with fundamentally different histories. It should be possible to maintain this unique feature of the pinewoods which are already regarded as a priceless heritage.

The native pinewood grant scheme is one of the major means of achieving this objective. In the scheme, the north-west and south-west regions have been designated 'exclusion zones', to prevent contamination of their highly unusual genetic compositions by material derived from other areas.

Future developments

The emphasis in the future will be:

- identification and exploitation of increasing levels of genetic gain;
- more rapid realisation of this gain by the forest industry.

To achieve these aims research into the following areas is being pursued and followed through into practice.

1. Creation of specific crosses (families) where both the male and female genotypes are known; identification of families where the genotypes combine to provide outstanding progeny; re-creation of these families by controlled pollination and multiplying-up of scarce seed using vegetative propagation.

2. Identification of site-specific families or genotypes. Currently genotypes are selected that perform well across a range of sites. As our knowledge of 1. above and vegetative propagation increases, it should be possible to select specific families or genotypes for specific sites, e.g. perform well on exposed sites, or nutrient deficient sites.

3. The use of different forms of screening of genotypes in the laboratory or nursery to test their suitability for various traits will continue, thereby reducing the dependence on costly, long-term field progeny tests, e.g. use of a frost chamber to test for frost tolerance, measuring photosynthetic efficiency as an indication of vigour.

4. Genotypes will increasingly be identified and pedigree authenticated, in biochemical terms (e.g. terpenes, isoenzymes, DNA). Research also continues to seek to identify biochemical markers produced naturally at an early stage by the specific genotype which can be related to other desirable attributes, e.g. insect resistance.

5. Knowledge of the mechanisms that control flowering continues in a range of species. If it becomes possible to control when a genotype flowers (both male and female) and the quantity of those flowers, more seed or propagules of the very best genetic material could be released into commerce quicker. One way in which this is being undertaken in Sitka spruce is in the establishment of approved seed orchards indoors, in huge polytunnels. In these tunnels the cultural treatments can be manipulated, increasing the number of flowers and thus the amount of improved seed.

6. Research is continuing into micropropagation. This involves multiplying-up high value genotypes within a laboratory environment. Work to date suggests possible multiplication rates of 100 000+ within one year. It has also been necessary to develop and thoroughly understand micropropagation methods as a means for taking advantage of other developments in biotechnology.

5   Establishment and tending

Objectives

The first essential before starting establishment operations is to decide on the objectives. Failure to make these clear from the outset will create difficulties and mistakes in all subsequent operations. Much forestry planting will have as its main objective the production of timber but there will be other important objectives concerned with landscape, conservation, recreation, sporting and shelter which may result in some reduction in timber producing capacity. Sometimes, such objectives will be paramount but rarely to the entire exclusion of timber production.

Timber production

It is necessary to consider the type of timber required, the length of time it will take to produce it and the potential markets, matters which are discussed in greater depth in Chapters 11, 12 and 13. With these in mind, it is possible to select species which will give the best yield for the sites concerned. In most cases, both quantity and quality of timber produced will be important. Obviously, problems will arise if substantial quantities of low grade (and therefore low value) material are produced, unless there is a suitable market in close proximity. Good quality sawlog material, whether coniferous or broadleaved, is much more likely to find a satisfactory market. In upland areas and on less fertile lowland sites, use of coniferous species will almost invariably give the best return. Good quality broadleaved timber can only be produced on the more fertile, less exposed, lowland sites – below about 250 m altitude. Coppice has had a major influence on broadleaved woodlands in the past and is still practised extensively with sweet chestnut in southeast England. Coppice is discussed at the end of this chapter.

Landscape

There are occasions when landscape improvement or maintenance will be an overriding objective. Usually, however, landscape will be a subordinate though still important consideration. In recent years people in this country have become increasingly interested in the appearance of the countryside and there have been justifiable objections to unsympathetic changes in landscape caused by insensitive afforestation or clear felling. Changes due to forestry activities can usually be blended into the landscape by paying proper attention to the shape of plantations related to the land form, the scale of the landscape, the need for diversity of colour and texture and the incorporation of natural features in the design. The principles are well explained in the Forestry Commission's *Forest landscape design guidelines*.

Wildlife conservation

It is important to give attention to conservation when setting overall objectives and this is discussed in greater detail in Chapter 8 'Wildlife management'. The level of priority will vary greatly. A site of unique conservation value, for example ancient

R.E. Crowther, former Principal Silviculturist (South), **A.J. Low**, former Principal Silviculturist (North), and **P.M. Tabbush**, Principal Silviculturist (South)

woodland whose history can be traced back to medieval times or earlier, may impose absolute constraints on forestry practice in the area. On the other hand, simple conservation measures involving little or no sacrifice of timber potential, such as keeping trees back from stream edges or mowing ride and road sides alternately in successive years, can be applied in most forestry schemes. Conservation will usually have some influence on choice of species. Wildlife conservation is considered in greater detail in the Forestry Commission's *Forest nature conservation guidelines.*

Recreation

This is discussed in greater detail in Chapter 16 'Recreation in the forest'. Like conservation, it needs to have a defined place in the objectives so that decisions on planting layout and choice of species can take into account present and possible future recreational needs.

Choice of species

Correct choice of species is essential if the selected objectives are to be met. In Britain climatic conditions are generally favourable for tree growth and a wide range of species will grow well. Before considering the influence of site factors, it is useful to examine the range of species available to the forester.

Exotic species

The introduction of exotic tree species into Britain has been stimulated by three factors, firstly the climate in Britain favours tree growth because of relatively mild winters and rainfall distributed throughout the year. Spring frosts and summer droughts may have a severe effect on newly planted trees but do not usually affect trees seriously after the establishment phase. Secondly, much poor land

available for planting has proved unsuitable for native trees while several introduced species grow well in difficult site conditions. The third factor is historical. Landowners were interested in establishing exotic trees in their arboreta and gardens and vied with one another to import and grow the latest discoveries as various countries were explored.

Apart from sycamore and sweet chestnut which have in fact become naturalised, there are no exotic broadleaved species with a role in forestry at present. There are some promising candidates which may become more widely planted, for example the southern beeches (*Nothofagus* species), particularly if the promise of more hardy seed origins is confirmed.

In the case of coniferous species, the position is very different because with the exception of Scots pine all the timber producing conifers used in British forestry have been introduced to this country.

NATIVE TREE SPECIES

These are the trees which colonised Britain unaided by the influence of man after the last Ice Age, about 10 000 years ago. This natural reinvasion of trees ceased when the English Channel opened some 6000 years ago. Trees which are regarded as native number about 30 depending on whether certain larger shrubs are considered to be trees. They are listed in Table 5.1. Of this total only a few are suitable for commercial timber production although a few more have wood of some interest for craftwork and decorative purposes. Generally, these trees do not have the ability to produce high yields of timber although individual values may still be high for timber of good quality (see Chapter 14).

Table 5.1 Native tree species

The trees generally accepted to be truly native are, in an approximate order of arrival here:

Common juniper	*Juniperus communis*
Downy birch	*Betula pubescens*
Silver birch	*Betula pendula*
Aspen	*Populus tremula*
Scots pine*	*Pinus sylvestris*
Bay willow	*Salix pentandra*
Common alder	*Alnus glutinosa*
Hazel	*Corylus avellana*
Small-leaved lime	*Tilia cordata*
Bird cherry	*Prunus padus*
Goat willow	*Salix caprea*
Wych elm	*Ulmus glabra*
Rowan	*Sorbus aucuparia*
Sessile oak*	*Quercus petraea*
Ash*	*Fraxinus excelsior*
Holly	*Ilex aquifolium*
Common oak*	*Quercus robur*
Hawthorn	*Crataegus monogyna*
Crack willow	*Salix fragilis*
Black poplar	*Populus nigra* var. *betulifolia*
Yew	*Taxus baccata*
Whitebeam	*Sorbus aria*
Midland thorn	*Crataegus laevigata*
Crab apple	*Malus sylvestris*
Wild cherry*	*Prunus avium*
Strawberry tree	*Arbutus unedo*
White willow	*Salix alba*
Field maple	*Acer campestre*
Wild service tree	*Sorbus torminalis*
Large-leaved lime	*Tilia platyphyllos*
Beech*	*Fagus sylvatica*
Hornbeam	*Carpinus betulus*
Box	*Betulus sempervirens*

*Important timber trees

Native trees

The classification 'Native Trees' does present some problems of definition because some species which clearly came into Britain through the influence of man are well established and sustain themselves naturally, sycamore and sweet chestnut being good examples. English elm is another, although in most parts of Britain this is now surviving only as hedgerow suckers because of the effect of Dutch elm disease on mature trees. There are also difficulties because some trees have a limited natural distribution in Britain. Beech, for instance, is not regarded as having spread naturally into northern England, most of Wales or Scotland. There are two other features of this native group of trees; firstly they include only three conifers, Scots pine, yew and juniper. Only Scots pine is an important timber tree though the wood of yew is extremely decorative and valued for this reason. Secondly, the number of broadleaved native trees capable of producing timber for industry is small and in comparison with many non-native species their yields are low. The average volume yield of all broadleaves in Britain is about 5 m^3 per hectare per year while that for the conifers is about 11 m^3 per hectare per year.

The category of native trees is helpful in the context of the conservation of semi-natural woodland and in the improvement of plantation forestry to meet wildlife management and conservation objectives. However, any attempt to confine forest planting to these species would affect forestry adversely by preventing the use of valuable, productive timber trees which are not necessarily harmful to conservation interests.

Varieties and cultivars

Although the numbers of varieties and cultivars of ornamental trees are very large, only cultivars of poplar have any present significance in forestry. European and American poplars have been crossed to produce a number of fast-growing disease-resistant varieties which have been successfully planted in lowland Britain. Cultivars of other species may assume more importance in the future as results of tree breeding are applied to forestry through the medium of vegetative propagation.

Provenance and seed origin

The process of determining which species were suited to conditions in Britain and which site factors influenced their growth was, in the early stages, one of trial and error. Later, systematic experimentation testing species and provenance on a range of different sites has given a better understanding of species performance in relation to site factors. Some species have a very wide natural distribution covering a range of climatic and site types and it is important to choose appropriate races and seed origins within that range to suit British conditions. Sitka spruce is a good example. It has a natural north–south distribution of some 1500 miles from Alaska to Oregon (from latitude 39° to 61° north). Its east–west distribution is restricted to coastal areas and it is not tolerant of low humidity, low rainfall or drought. The more northerly origins are adapted to a short growing season with long day-length and in Britain are slow growers (although tolerant of spring frosts). The southern origins are more vigorous but because they start to grow early in spring they are susceptible in Britain to spring frost damage. In practice, Sitka spruce seed origins from the middle of the range are well suited to most conditions in the north and west of Britain, Queen Charlotte Islands

being amongst the best. However, in the south-west and including much of Wales, Washington origins have the edge.

Distribution of species

The Forestry Commission's 1979–82 Census of Woodlands shows that there has been a tendency to concentrate on a small number of species in Britain. In coniferous high forest, Sitka spruce, Norway spruce, Scots, lodgepole and Corsican pines account for 80% of the area. The principal broadleaved species are oak, beech, sycamore, ash and birch, which together make up 77% of the total broad-leaved area of high forest.

Site factors

Factors which have a marked influence on tree establishment and subsequent growth are soil, local climate and topography. Different tree species are adapted to different conditions. Within species, differences in races or provenances are important. However, there is a risk of making the process of matching species and site over-complicated and the use of a wide range of species is likely to introduce management and marketing problems. Some species, Sitka spruce and sycamore for example, can grow reasonably well on a wide range of sites.

Soil

Classification of soils for forestry is concerned with the physical properties that influence root development and hence tree stability, and with the chemical properties which affect nutrient availability. Soil classification for forestry, therefore, places emphasis on physical factors such as depth of soil, soil water regime and aeration, and the presence of compacted or cemented layers which limit downward rooting.

These factors not only control root growth but they may also affect root function, i.e. the ability to take up water and dissolved nutrients. The ability of the soil to provide nutrients therefore depends on these factors as well as on the mineral composition of the soil material, whether this be derived from the bedrock itself or drift material deposited by ice, water or wind. Table 5.3 summarises species choice according to a simplified soil classification. Brief descriptions of these soils follow.

Brown earths
Freely drained, usually loamy textured soils that are slightly or moderately acid in reaction. They are fertile and usually provide favourable rooting conditions but are liable to encourage strong weed growth of bramble or bracken.

Podzols
These are also freely drained soils with good rooting conditions but are strongly acid and are less fertile than brown earths. Textures are usually sandy and it is convenient to include in this group other sandy textured brown earths and coastal soils. Heather vegetation is typical of this group.

Ironpan soils
These are mainly upland soils with a perched water table above the thin cemented ironpan and often with a peaty surface layer. Aeration is readily improved by cultivation and by tree growth itself but fertility is usually rather low. Heather, mat grass or purple moor grass are typical.

Lowland gleys
These are mainly heavy clay soils often calcareous in the subsoil but also included are groundwater gleys of lighter texture. Poor aeration in winter restricts

Disc trencher on restock site.

rooting to the topsoil except for well adapted species such as alders and oak. The soils are usually fertile and very weedy especially after clear felling. Grassy vegetation, especially tufted hair grass is usual.

Upland gleys and peaty gleys
Textures are clays or loams in which the heavy rainfall maintains a high water table for much of the year. A shallow (less than 45 cm) peat layer forms on the wettest sites. Rooting is restricted in depth. Nutrition is usually adequate on non-peaty gleys although the application of phosphate may be beneficial on peaty gleys. Tufted hair grass is characteristic of non-peaty gleys with purple moor grass on peaty gleys.

Peatlands; flushed and basin bogs
These are sites with an impermeable substrate where peat has accumulated under the influence of water

Table 5.2 Area of high forest by principal species and countries (1982); all woodland ownerships

Species	England Area (ha)	Percentage of category	of all species	Wales Area (ha)	Percentage of category	of all species	Scotland Area (ha)	Percentage of category	of all species	Great Britain Area (ha)	Percentage of category	of all species
Scots pine	91 074	24	11	5 592	3	2	144 371	19	17	241 037	18	13
Corsican pine	40 212	10	5	3 693	2	2	3 346	<1	<1	47 251	4	2
Lodgepole pine	15 249	4	2	7 895	5	3	103 924	13	12	127 068	10	7
Sitka spruce	75 599	20	9	85 701	51	38	364 601	48	44	525 901	40	28
Norway spruce	43 499	11	5	18 641	11	8	54 707	7	7	116 847	9	6
European larch	21 862	6	3	2 595	2	1	15 957	2	2	40 414	3	2
Jap./hybrid larch	35 742	9	5	23 461	14	10	52 146	7	6	111 349	8	6
Douglas fir	25 063	6	3	10 708	6	5	11 628	2	1	47 399	4	2
Other conifers	17 442	4	2	7 906	5	4	6 312	1	1	31 660	2	2
Mixed conifers	21 665	6	3	1 744	1	1	8 641	1	1	32 050	2	2
Total conifers	387 407	100	48	167 936	100	74	765 633	100	91	1 320 976	100	70
Oak	129 352	30	16	26 087	44	11	16 551	22	2	171 990	31	9
Beech	57 828	14	7	5 612	10	2	10 496	14	1	73 936	13	4
Sycamore	36 204	9	4	3 833	6	2	9 389	12	1	49 426	9	3
Ash	56 092	13	7	9 387	16	4	4 102	5	1	69 581	12	4
Birch	45 901	11	6	5 583	9	2	16 647	22	2	68 131	12	4
Poplar	12 757	3	2	504	1	<1	329	<1	<1	13 590	2	1
Sweet chestnut	9 451	2	1	412	1	<1	8	<1	<1	9 871	2	<1
Elm	5 545	1	1	358	1	<1	3 611	5	<1	9 514	2	<1
Other broadleaves	20 294	5	2	3 718	6	2	5 115	7	1	29 127	5	2
Mixed broadleaves	50 914	12	6	3 851	6	2	10 319	13	1	65 084	12	3
Total broadleaves	424 338	100	52	59 345	100	26	76 567	100	9	560 250	100	30
Total	811 745		100	227 281		100	842 200		100	1 881 226		100

Table 5.3 Soils and species choice

Soil	Soil codes*	Conifer species		Broadleaved species (sheltered sites only)	Remarks
		Sheltered	Exposed		
Brown earths (loams)	1, 12t	Douglas fir Larches	Sitka spruce	Beech Oak Sycamore	Most tree species will grow well on this soil type.
Podzols and other sandy soils	3, 15	Scots pine Corsican pine Larches Sitka spruce	Sitka spruce (Lodgepole pine)	Birch	Sitka spruce and Douglas fir may suffer heather check unless planted in mixture with pine or larch.
Ironpan soils	4	Sitka spruce	Sitka spruce	Birch	Mixtures of spruce and pine or larch may be used.
Lowland gleys	5, 7	Corsican pine Norway spruce	Corsican pine Norway spruce	Oak Alder Birch	
Upland gleys and peaty soils		Sitka spruce Norway spruce (where non-peaty)	Sitka spruce Norway spruce (where non-peaty)	Birch Oak (where non-peaty)	
Peatlands and flushed basin bogs	8, 9	Sitka spruce	Sitka spruce	Birch	Birch for amenity and conservation only.
Peatlands, raised, flat or blanket bogs	10, 11	Sitka spruce Lodgepole pine	Sitka spruce Lodgepole pine		Mixtures of Sitka spruce with pines or larch may be used.
Calcareous soils	12a, 12b	Corsican pine	Corsican pine	Beech Norway maple Sycamore	Where free calcium carbonate is present in the topsoil most species will suffer lime-induced chlorosis.

*See Appendix to Chapter 3 in Forestry Commission Bulletin 62 *Silviculture of broadleaved woodland.*

seepage from nearby higher ground. This flushing water brings nutrients which become incorporated into the peat via the bog vegetation. The vegetation contains the tall species of rush and usually purple moor grass.

Peatlands; raised, flat or blanket bogs

Peat, which accumulates in the absence of flushing, has a low nutrient content and carries a 'bare ground' vegetation that is tolerant both of the waterlogging and poor nutrition. Such species include deer sedge (*Trichophorum*), cotton grass (*Eriophorum*), heather, cross leaved heath and several sphagnum moss species. Characteristically purple moor grass is absent from these sites although on blanket bogs unflushed and flushed areas often occur in close proximity.

Calcareous soils

These are found on the chalk and limestone rocks mainly in lowland England. When shallow to bedrock and calcareous to the surface they provide difficult conditions for tree growth because of lime-induced chlorosis. Deeper soils with high pH restricted to the subsoil behave similarly to the non-calcareous brown earths.

Exposure

This is related to elevation but topography plays a major part. Hillsides are more exposed than valleys at the same elevation while low ground with no shelter by hills or trees can also be extremely exposed. On exposed sites early establishment of trees may be difficult. At a later stage tree crops may be susceptible to windthrow and this can be a serious problem on upland areas with shallow soils which restrict rooting depth (see Chapter 10). Exposure problems close to the sea are exacerbated by salt laden storm winds.

Table 5.3 is a simplified guide to species choice by grouping the main soil types from Pyatt's classification, showing for each soil group only the species most commonly planted in large-scale forestry.

The individual characteristics of a range of tree species in relation to site, timber qualities and yield are given in the Appendix to this Chapter.

Establishment methods

If bare land is being afforested the only practical method available in most circumstances is the planting of young trees raised in a nursery. Very rarely direct sowing of seed or the insertion of unrooted cuttings may be used. If there is an existing tree crop then two other alternatives are available for establishing a new crop: the use of natural regeneration or (with some broadleaved species) coppice.

Successful direct sowing with pine seed has been achieved on heathland sites, particularly with Scots pine. Good weed control, typically by burning and ploughing beforehand, is essential. Direct sowing of acorns has also resulted in successful establishment. However, the risk of heavy losses from predation by birds and small mammals is high. Frost lift on mineral soils can be a problem with small conifer seedlings and the control of weed competition is difficult. On balance, direct sowing is regarded as unreliable in most circumstances and is an extravagant use of valuable seed.

The use of nursery transplants which typically spend 1–2 years in the seedbeds and 1–2 years in transplant lines is the usual practice in Britain. Survival may be expected to be very high (90%), provided the plants are carefully treated from lifting in the nursery until they have been safely planted in the forest. Particular difficulties are presented by large-scale handling, and these must be overcome by instituting systems which avoid rough handling,

Mounder.

desiccation, heating or cold storage damage. This subject is dealt with in more detail in Forestry Commission Bulletin 76 *Silvicultural principles for upland restocking*.

The use of improved genetic material is of increasing importance for high yielding species (see Chapter 4), and this is often produced as rooted cuttings, to maximise the number of outplants obtained from a restricted supply of valuable improved seed. Only with poplars and willows is the use of unrooted cuttings a practical proposition and their use must be accompanied by adequate ground cultivation.

Where a tree crop is to be replaced, natural regeneration is a possibility and with many broadleaved species coppicing is an option. However, there are two main disadvantages. Firstly, seed years are intermittent and unpredictable with most species, typically 5 years or so with oak and beech, rather more frequently with conifers. This makes relying on natural regeneration difficult in most situations where the timing of the felling programme is controlled by market factors. Secondly, natural regeneration and coppice provide no opportunity for change of species or the introduction of improved genetic stock, although they do conserve the local stock which may be important for wildlife conservation.

However, establishment costs are low when advantage can be taken of natural regeneration. It is important to ensure that dense thickets of natural regeneration have their stocking reduced at an early stage otherwise heavy snowfalls may cause high losses due to stem breakage.

Establishment is the most costly period in the sequence of operations needed to manage a plantation and methods, therefore, need to be carefully appraised. Each operation should be considered in order to ensure that the right intensity and timing is chosen.

Ground preparation

Clearance of restock sites

A great deal depends on the amount of lop and top on the ground and what cultural operations are planned. If there is heavy branchwood arising from felling a previous broadleaved crop then it is advisable to cut and remove the larger material for firewood and burn the remainder. This work should be carried out as part of the felling operation. Leaving lop and top to be cleared later invariably leads to a much more difficult and expensive operation and if no clearing is done subsequent weed control becomes virtually impossible. Conifer tops and branches are lighter and it is often possible to plant through them without further treatment (particularly if they are left to decay before planting) although extra planting costs will usually be incurred and a good standard of planting can be difficult to maintain. The brash which is often accumulated in windrows to assist the harvesting operation may seriously impede planting. Site preparation using scarification and mounding offers the most cost-effective means of ensuring the availability of enough well-distributed microsites suitable for planting.

Drainage and cultivation

Waterlogged soils are usually in this condition because they are fine textured or very compact in the subsoil and movement of soil water through them is very slow. It follows that drains on such soil types (most peats and gleys) will only remove substantial amounts of water from the upper more permeable layers. Where there is a restricted horizontal movement of water through the soil deeper drains at closer spacing are unlikely to solve the problem. Spacing between drains should vary with the slope from 20 m on deep peat with slopes of less than 3° to 50 m on steep loamy gleys. However, it is important to have a drainage system which removes surface water and does not allow it to accumulate in hollows or in plough furrows. The layout of a main drain system must take into account the catchment area it will serve. If the catchment is too large heavy rainfall will overburden the drain, causing erosion. If too small then the drain will not have sufficient flow to keep itself clear of blockages. The optimum slope along a drain is about 2° which is steep enough to ensure rapid water movement and minimise silting but not so steep as to cause serious erosion. Drains should run towards the head of the valley when draining slopes, this gives the shortest length of drain for a given catchment area and allows better control of the slope of the drain as it approaches the watercourse.

Successful tree planting on many peaty soils was achieved in the 1920s and 30s by planting on up-turned turves which provided an adequately drained microsite on which the tree could establish itself. Ploughing to provide a raised turf for planting is now the common form of forest cultivation. Once establishment is achieved tree roots are an effective way of drawing moisture out of impervious peats and clays and this can result in a drying and cracking process which is not reversed even in winter. Unfortunately, after felling the presence of tree roots makes it very expensive to plough restocking sites to provide raised furrows for replanting.

Large-scale (30 m wide × 1.5 m high) ridge and furrow landforms are commonly used in reclamation schemes in Britain to aid the removal of excess winter rainfall and improve rooting conditions. Investigations of soil, physical and hydrological properties in relation to tree growth have shown that this system can succeed in producing land with reduced

FORESTS AND WATER GUIDELINES

The Forestry Commission's publication *Forests and water guidelines* is essential reading for managers who look after forest and woodland in the catchments of streams and river systems. The guidelines recognise the importance of the aquatic environment and the importance of maintaining good quality. There is particular emphasis on the uplands of Britain where rivers, lakes and water supply reservoirs are most likely to be affected by land use changes. Such changes could also become important in the lowlands.

waterlogging and improved tree growth. The results support the use of the ridge and furrow system in areas where rainfall is high and soil moisture deficits low, but a modified system of lower amplitude may be warranted in drier areas.

Many potential forest soils are impervious to water and root penetration because they are either heavily compacted by the effect of the last ice age or have developed a pan resulting from deposition of iron compounds at depths between 10 cm and 40 cm. Deep ploughing using a specially designed plough was found in the later 1930s to be an answer to this. Modern ploughs for mineral soils usually have a deep subsoiler or ripper combined with a shallow mould board which produces an upturned ridge and hence a well drained weed-free planting position. Complete ploughing is seldom used in forestry but may have a place on highly indurated soils.

Excavator mounding.

Disc trencher.

Scarification and mounding

Site preparation for restocking which involves cultivation has increased markedly over recent years. Cultivation can provide suitable sites for planting, enhancing survival and early growth. There are special problems in the restocking of clear felled sites and experiments and operational experience with Sitka spruce have shown that satisfactory survival and early growth can be achieved without cultivation. However, this can only be achieved where the plants used are of an adequate size with a high root growth potential, and are carefully handled, planted and maintained. Cultivation may still be desirable to provide sufficient evenly distributed planting positions to meet stocking standards and to assist root spread for enhancing future stability. For species such as Douglas fir, Corsican pine or where poor plant handling may have reduced root growth potential, cultivation improves survival and early growth. The benefits are a result of improved aeration and more favourable soil temperatures, and also reduced weed competition on some sites.

Scarifiers and mounders provide improved planting sites without major site disturbance, so reducing the potential for soil erosion and subsequent sedimentation and turbidity in watercourses. They were initially developed in Scandinavia to encourage natural regeneration but more recently they have been used there and in Great Britain to aid restocking by cultivating ground prior to replanting. Scarifiers and mounders offer the prospect of good planting sites at a lower cost than ploughs on most clear felled areas.

Scarifiers and mounders can be split into four main groups:

Mound produced by excavator mounding.

Scarifiers	Mounders
1. Patch scarifier.	1. Continuous acting mounder.
2. Disc trencher.	2. Excavator mounder.

The choice of machine type is governed by the soil types present. In Great Britain it is convenient to distinguish between the requirements of (1) poorly drained soils including the peats, peaty gleys and other gleys; and (2) freely drained soils, including brown earths, podzols, ironpans and some sands.

Poorly drained soils (with slopes of 3° or more)

On these a raised, aerated and weed-free planting site is desirable. This is provided on large-scale sites by the continuous acting mounders, with the quality of mound produced being greatly improved by the presence of a layer of vegetation or mineral soil and lack of brash. Excavator mounding is also appropriate.

Poorly drained soils (with slopes less than 3°)

These require a raised planting site. As water will tend to collect in these areas the mounds are best produced by an excavator during site drainage. The mounds can be placed on top of light brash or the bucket of the excavator can be used to make holes in brash mats before the mound is placed there. The drains which are created to produce the mounds can be linked to the main drainage system.

Freely drained soils

On these a planting site free of surface vegetation and with the mineral soil exposed is desirable. Patch scarifiers can only cope with light brash such as that from larch and pine. Lightweight disc trenchers also operate best in light brash and may require two or three passes to achieve a good degree of cultivation as well as brash dispersal. A heavier (powered) disc trencher will clear brash and produce broad shallow and continuous scrapes on most freely drained sites.

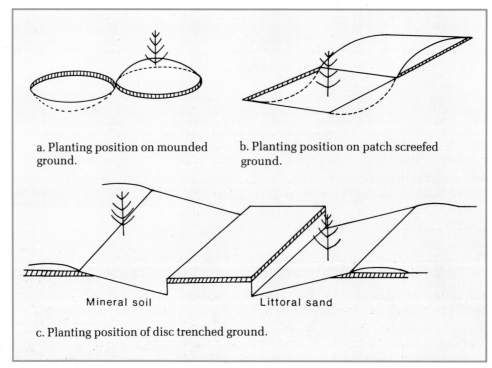

a. Planting position on mounded ground.

b. Planting position on patch screefed ground.

Mineral soil   Littoral sand

c. Planting position of disc trenched ground.

FIGURE 5.1 Diagrammatic illustrations of planting position for cultivation type. (Hatched areas depict original ground surface.)

Planting position

To obtain the full benefit from cultivation, the planting position should be carefully chosen (Figure 5.1).

Poorly drained soils

Planting should usually be on top of the mound at approximately 30 cm height. On larger mounds the tree should be planted on a step cut at 30 cm above the original ground level. Where a mound is incomplete, then the highest weed-free position should be planted.

Freely drained soils

On mounds the planting position is the same as for wet soils. With scarification, planting is best carried out in the middle of the shallow patch and the higher outside edge of the trench. On very freely drained soils such as littoral sands good survival has been achieved when planting on the higher outside edge of the trench and midway down the trench.

Planning

It is essential to match the equipment to the soil type and related cultivation needs, the scale of the site and the sensitivity of the species being planted. The cost of silvicultural operations and quality of establishment achieved are strongly influenced by the harvesting operation. Costs of both should be optimised by careful planning.

Fencing and tree protection

Both farm and wild animals can seriously damage young plantations and fencing is one way of preventing this. However, fencing is expensive. Careful planning is required to ensure that it is only used where essential and that the most economical and

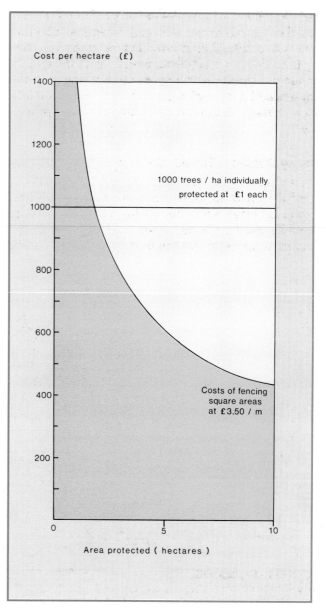

FIGURE 5.2 Comparative costs of protection with individual tree guards (straight line) and fencing (curve).

55

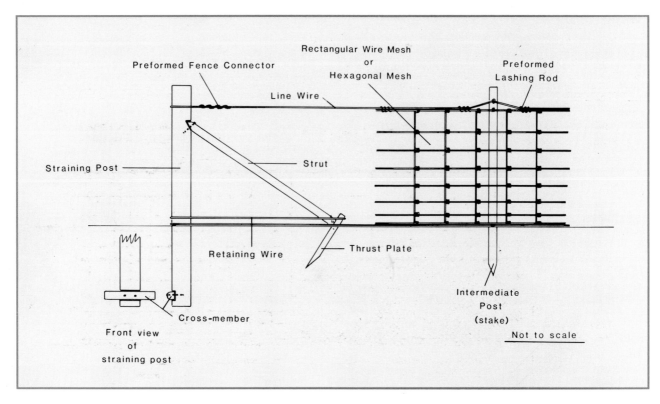

Straining Post

Preformed Fence Connector

Line Wire

Rectangular Wire Mesh
or
Hexagonal Mesh

Preformed
Lashing Rod

Strut

Retaining Wire

Thrust Plate

Cross-member

Front view
of
straining post

Intermediate
Post
(stake)

Not to scale

effective specification is adopted. Protection of the young plantation may not be the only consideration. Although the owner of farm animals is required by law to keep them under control and to fence against his own stock, many conveyances include clauses which require a woodland owner to maintain a stock fence on the boundary. There may be other legal constraints such as rights of way, both public and private, though usually these can be satisfied by the use of gates, stiles or cattle grids at the appropriate places.

Fencing may be unnecessary because there are no damaging animals present or because numbers can

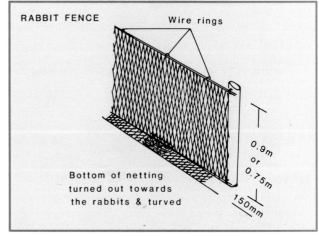

RABBIT FENCE

Wire rings

Bottom of netting
turned out towards
the rabbits & turved

0.9m
or
0.75m

150mm

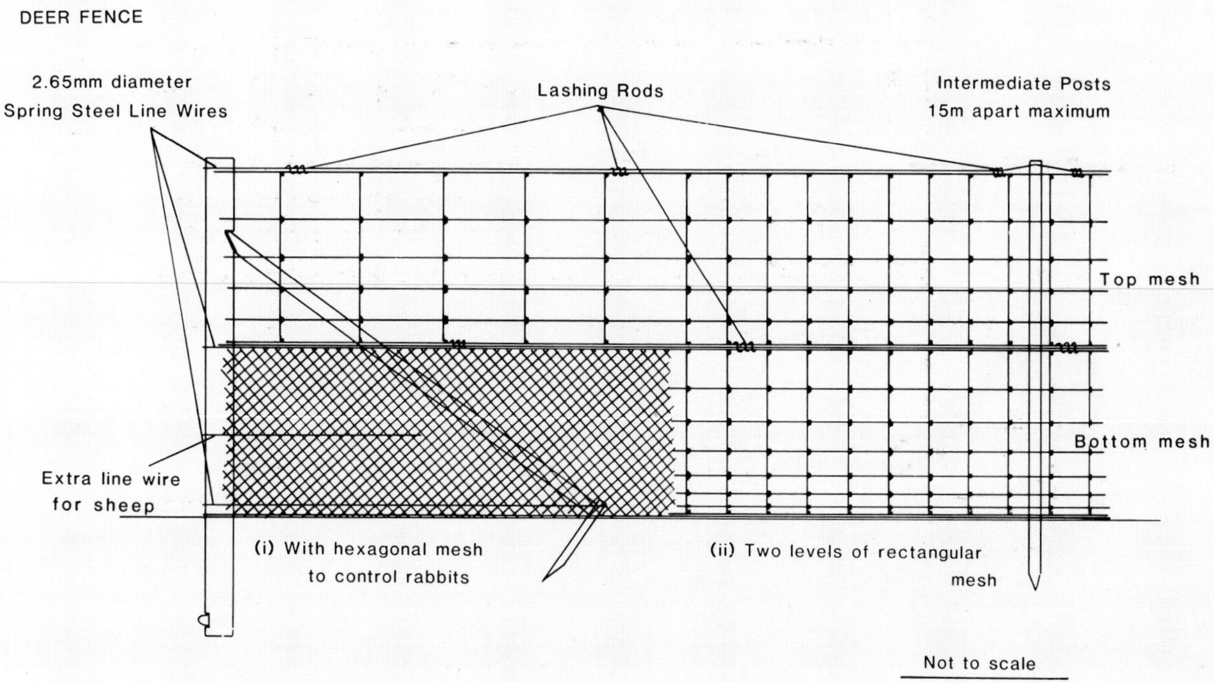

DEER FENCE

2.65mm diameter
Spring Steel Line Wires

Lashing Rods

Intermediate Posts
15m apart maximum

Top mesh

Bottom mesh

Extra line wire
for sheep

(i) With hexagonal mesh
to control rabbits

(ii) Two levels of rectangular
mesh

Not to scale

FIGURE 5.3 A range of typical fence specifications.

57

be reduced to levels causing little damage. Rabbits are a case in point. There will also be instances when the cost of fencing would be so high that it is cheaper to provide individual protection for each tree than to fence the whole area. Each case will depend on the area, length and type of fence involved and the number and cost of individual tree protection. In Figure 5.2 the cost per hectare of fencing areas between 1 ha and 10 ha is compared with the cost of protecting either 500 or 1000 trees per hectare against deer and rabbits. Additional advantages of individual tree protection include less interference with game bird management and the possible revenue from roe deer.

Individual tree protection can take the form of wire or plastic mesh cylindrical guards which prevent damage by rabbits and roe deer. Alternatively, the popular plastic treeshelter can be used and this not only protects the tree from mammal damage but also enhances early growth of the tree. The shelters also facilitate weed control because trees are easily found and the shelters prevent accidental herbicide damage to the young trees. Further details can be found in Forestry Commission Handbook 7 *Treeshelters*.

Fence specification

Spring steel wire is now recommended for all forest fences and mild steel is not used. Spring steel has the advantage that once tensioned in a fence it has the ability to accept further accidental tensioning from animals or humans or trees without deforming. Once the accidental load is removed the fence returns to its original position and tension. Multiple wires are not used in spring steel fences but netting of various sizes depending on the animals constrained is used instead. Because spring steel fences retain tension well the spacing of the supporting fence posts can be

increased substantially, thus reducing both material and erection costs.

The fencing specification must match in height and strength the animals it is wished to constrain. Figure 5.3 illustrates a range of typical fencing. These and other designs are given in Forestry Commission Bulletin 102 *Forest fencing*. Expected fence life is a further consideration. Wooden posts and rails must be pressure treated with preservative if the fence is to be permanent but untreated wood can be used for a temporary fence.

Planting

Spacing

A number of factors influence the decision of spacing at time of planting and over the last 40 years there has been a steady trend to widen spacing from 1.4 m to between 2 m and 3 m. However, for Sitka spruce recent wood quality studies have shown that it is probably unwise to exceed a 2 m spacing if structural quality sawnwood is to be produced.

The advantages of using a wide spacing compared with a closer one are:

- reduced costs of cultivation, plants and planting;
- increase in individual tree size.

The disadvantages of increasing spacing are:

- losses of plants cause large gaps;
- canopy closure and full site utilisation takes longer;
- branch suppression is delayed leading to larger knots and reduced timber quality;
- more rapid diameter growth results in wider annual rings and greater taper;
- the smaller tree population allows less intensive selection of good quality stems at time of thinning.

The spacing adopted must be a matter of judgement on the part of the forester after taking these factors into account for the site and crop involved.

When restocking broadleaved woodland, existing woody growth arising from natural regeneration and coppice regrowth can to some extent take the place of part of the planting allowing the forester to obtain the advantages of wider spacing without incurring all of the disadvantages. The variety of woody growth can be very wide and each site will need to be treated individually. However, two things can be said. First, it is essential to make sure that existing woody growth does not damage the planted trees and second, provided that full stocking conditions have been effectively achieved by the use of existing woody growth, then the crop can be treated subsequently in the standard way for thinning age and intensity although removals will of course be of non-crop species, at least at the first thinning.

Plant type

There are several plant type possibilities. The tradition in Britain is to use a bare-rooted transplant raised from seed, spending 1–2 years in seedbeds then being transplanted for a further 1–2 years. Transplants are described as 1+1, 2+2, 1+2, etc., depending on the years spent in seedbeds and transplant lines. Typically such plants are 200–400 mm in height with a root system in balance with the crown and a sturdy stem diameter. The British Standard BS 3936 : Part 4 : 1984 provides the standard nursery stock specification for forest trees (see Tables 5.4 and 5.5).

The effect of transplanting in the nursery is to stimulate the production of a compact fibrous root system. Undercutting in the nursery seedbeds is an alternative to transplanting and if correctly carried out is a satisfactory method. Two-year-old and 3-year-old undercut plants are referred to as 1u1 and 1u1u1 respectively. Since 1983 research trials have been carried out to develop a successful precision sowing and undercutting regime for a number of conifer species. Undercut plants generally are sturdier and have a more favourable shoot to root ratio than non-undercut transplants. Undercut stock also appears capable of withstanding cold storage better than transplants. In forest experiments undercut plants generally show as good survival rate as transplants and in Douglas fir performance is markedly better.

Generally smaller plants are preferred for planting in exposed localities while larger ones are used on the more fertile sites where regrowth is greater and exposure less. The use of seedlings (i.e. 1+0 or 2+0) which have not been transplanted or undercut incurs the risk of severe losses due to the small size, low reserves or imbalance between root and shoot in these plants.

Plants raised in small containers, typically the Japanese paper pots, have been extensively tested. Containers may be particularly useful for improving the establishment of sensitive species such as Corsican pine and Douglas Fir. Trials since 1986 have established that Douglas fir and Sitka spruce seedlings of plantable size can be produced within one year in a range of container types when grown in polythene greenhouses. Such seedlings have performed well in forest experiments suggesting that further trials of this production method are warranted. Container raised Corsican pine is used in East Anglia because the system fits in well with mechanised planting and because the use of containers extends the planting season. Corsican pine is a difficult species to plant and survival can be poor although the use of container plants does not always overcome this difficulty. Container raised eucalypts have been very successful in trials.

Table 5.4   Minimum dimensions for open ground stock (from BS 3936)

Species	Minimum height	Minimum collar diameter for heights not less than								
		75	100	150	200	250	300	400	500	600
	mm	*mm*	*mm*	*mm*	*mm*	*mm*	*mm*	*mm*	*mm*	*mm*
Alder										
common alder	300	–	–	–	–	–	5.0	6.0	7.5	9.0
grey alder	300	–	–	–	–	–	4.5	5.0	6.0	7.0
Italian alder	300	–	–	–	–	–	4.5	5.0	6.0	7.0
Ash	200	–	–	–	5.0	5.5	6.5	8.0	9.5	11.0
Beech	200	–	–	–	4.0	4.5	5.0	6.0	7.5	9.0
Birch										
common silver birch	200	–	–	–	3.0	3.5	4.0	4.5	5.5	6.5
Chestnut										
sweet chestnut	200	–	–	–	5.0	5.5	6.5	8.0	9.5	11.0
Cypress										
Lawson cypress	200	–	–	–	4.0	4.5	5.0	6.5	7.5	8.5
Fir										
Douglas fir	200	–	–	–	3.0	3.5	4.0	5.0	6.0	–
grand fir	100	–	4.5	4.5	5.0	6.0	6.4	8.0	9.5	–
noble fir	100	–	5.0	5.0	5.0	6.0	6.5	8.0	9.5	–
Gean	200	–	–	–	5.0	5.5	6.5	8.0	9.5	11.0
Hemlock										
western hemlock	200	–	–	–	2.5	3.0	3.5	4.0	5.0	5.5
Larch										
European larch	200	–	–	–	2.5	3.5	4.0	5.0	6.0	6.5
hybrid larch	200	–	–	–	2.5	3.5	4.0	5.0	6.0	6.5
Japanese larch	200	–	–	–	2.5	3.5	4.0	5.0	6.0	6.5

Table 5.4   Minimum dimensions for open ground stock (from BS 3936) *(continued)*

Species	Minimum height	Minimum collar diameter for heights not less than								
		75	100	150	200	250	300	400	500	600
	mm	*mm*	*mm*	*mm*	*mm*	*mm*	*mm*	*mm*	*mm*	*mm*
Lime										
large-leaved lime	200	–	–	–	5.0	5.5	6.5	8.0	9.5	11.0
small-leaved lime	200	–	–	–	5.0	5.5	6.5	8.0	9.5	11.0
Maple										
Norway maple	200	–	–	–	3.5	4.0	4.5	5.0	6.0	7.0
sycamore	300	–	–	–	–	–	4.5	5.0	6.0	7.0
Oak										
sessile	200	–	–	–	5.0	5.5	6.5	8.0	9.5	11.0
Pine										
Bishop pine	100	–	3.0	4.0	4.5	5.5	6.5	8.0	9.5	–
Corsican pine	75	3.0	3.0	4.0	4.5	5.5	6.5	8.0	9.5	–
lodgepole pine	100	–	3.0	4.0	4.5	5.5	6.5	8.0	9.5	–
Scots pine	100	–	3.0	4.0	4.5	5.5	6.5	8.0	9.5	–
shore pine	100	–	3.0	4.0	4.5	5.5	6.5	8.0	9.5	–
Southern beech										
rauli	200	–	–	–	4.5	5.0	5.5	6.0	7.5	9.0
roble	200	–	–	–	4.5	5.0	5.5	6.0	7.5	9.0
Spruce										
Norway spruce	150	–	–	3.0	4.0	4.5	5.0	6.5	8.0	9.5
Sitka spruce	150	–	–	2.5	3.0	3.5	4.0	5.0	6.0	7.0
Sycamore (see under maple)										
Western red cedar	200	–	–	–	4.0	4.5	5.0	6.5	7.5	8.5

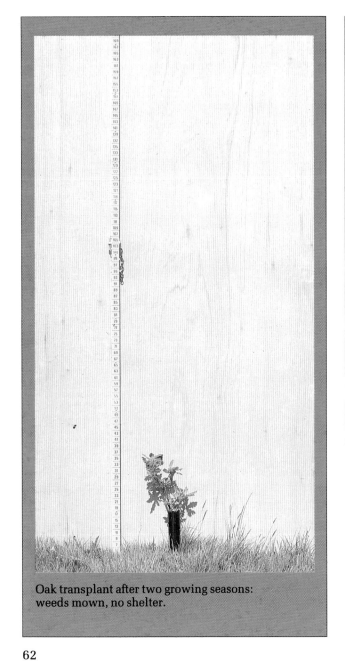

Oak transplant after two growing seasons: weeds mown, no shelter.

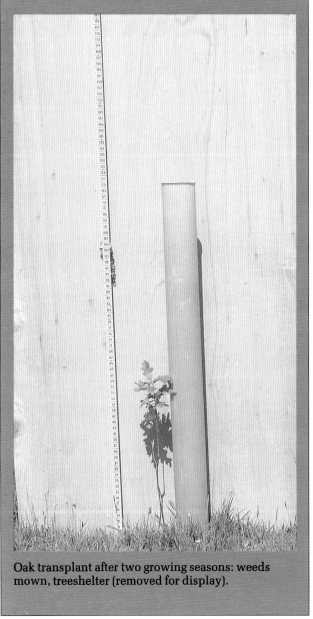

Oak transplant after two growing seasons: weeds mown, treeshelter (removed for display).

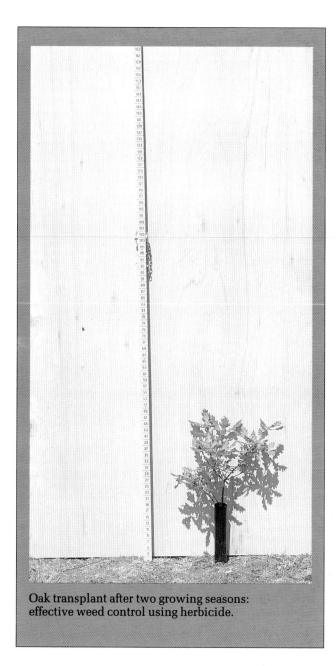

Oak transplant after two growing seasons: effective weed control using herbicide.

Oak transplant after two growing seasons: effective weed control plus treeshelter (removed for display).

63

Table 5.5   Minimum dimensions for container grown stock and container sizes (from BS 3936)

Species		Minimum height	Minimum collar diameter	Minimum container size*
		mm	*mm*	*ml*
Alder	common alder	600	6	125
	grey alder	600	6	125
	Italian alder	600	6	125
Ash		600	6	235
Beech		300	5	235
Birch	common silver birch	600	6	125
Chestnut	sweet chestnut	600	6	235
Fir	Douglas fir	200	3	100
Limes	large-leaved lime	600	6	235
	small-leaved lime	600	6	235
Maple	Norway maple	600	6	235
	sycamore	600	6	235
Oak	sessile	300	6	235
Pine	Corsican pine	120	2	100
	lodgepole pine	200	4	100
	Scots pine	200	4	100
Southern beech	rauli	600	6	125
	roble	600	6	125
Spruce	Norway spruce	200	4	100
	Sitka spruce	200	3	100
Sycamore	(see under maple)	–	–	–

*If the plants are grown in Japanese paper pots (JPPs) the following size designations for containers are appropriate:
100 mL   F408   125 mL   F508   235 mL   F515

Note: Extracts from BS 3936 : Part 4 : 1984 (1989) are reproduced with the permission of BSI. Complete copies can be obtained by post from BSI Sales, Linford Wood, Milton Keynes, MK14 6LE; telefax 0908 320856, telex 825777 BSIMK G.

Tending

Beating up

Some losses after planting are almost inevitable due to mammal, insect or fungal damage, or even fire. Summer drought can take a toll in very dry years, but much so-called drought damage is the result of poor root response after planting, occasioned by inadequate planting stock quality and poor plant-handling practices. It is not worth replacing failures unless the gaps are substantial, and it should be done as soon as the failures become apparent. This is unlikely to be before the survivors are at least 1 or probably 2 years old, the new plants will then be at a disadvantage and risk being suppressed. This can be mitigated to some extent by using larger plants, or even a faster growing species (hybrid larch is often used to beat up in Douglas fir).

It should be remembered that delayed beating up will extend the period over which weeding will be necessary. The conclusion is that the best course is to adopt high standards of plant handling in the initial planting so as to minimise or better still eliminate the need for beating up.

Weed control

Traditional forestry practice has been to cut any weeds which might shade the crop trees too strongly or which could cause physical damage by collapsing on them in winter. Before the advent of herbicides, weed cutting was the only practical way of controlling weed growth after planting. In recent weeding experiments, however, it has been found that cutting weeds does little to reduce competition for moisture and nutrients and may even increase it. Root competition reduces tree growth. On dry sites or in dry years it actually reduces the survival of newly planted trees. Competition is most detrimental if the trees have already been stressed, for example by poor planting or desiccation during transport from the nursery.

On many upland sites where new planting is undertaken, weed reinvasion after ploughing is sufficiently slow to allow satisfactory crop establishment with no further weed control, but herbicide control will be needed on many unploughed restocking sites. Most lowland sites, even when ploughed, will require chemical weed control.

Mechanical weeding with a tractor-mounted swipe or with a clearing saw can be effective in breaking down woody vegetation, but it is generally more effective to control woody growth with herbicides *before* planting. The herbicides which are effective in controlling dense woody weed growth are also likely to damage any forest trees already present.

In herbaceous vegetation, a weed-free area of about 1 m diameter has been shown to give cost-effective relief from competition, whilst also minimising the amount of herbicide used per hectare. This approach, however, is unlikely to be effective on tall, dense broadleaved herbaceous vegetation which can develop on very fertile lowland soils. As competition is most serious during spring and early summer, weeding in mid summer or later will have little effect in that growing season although it will help the trees in the following year provided there is little weed reinvasion.

There are many herbicides available which will control weeds in forestry. They work in a variety of ways some entering through the leaves of weeds, others through their roots. They must be applied before the trees are planted or when the trees are at a non-vulnerable stage or else the trees must be guarded. An alternative which is proving popular in forestry practice is to use direct applicators (weed wipes) to place the herbicide on to the weeds. It should be remembered that a successful herbicide application is often followed by a change of weed

Conifers also benefit from effective weed control. The Douglas fir on the left shows signs of nutrient deficiency in a mown sward. The Douglas fir on the right has benefited from a 1 m herbicide spot.

Table 5.6 Fertiliser prescriptions for Sitka spruce in upland Britain. The table shows suggested nutritional inputs for Sitka spruce in the pre-canopy closure stage. The prescriptions are representative of the sort of inputs necessary to bring Sitka spruce to canopy closure in a condition where nutrient deficiencies are not limiting growth.

Soil type		At planting	Year 4	6	8	9	12	15	16
Brown earth Surface water gley Intergrade		(P)	Heather control if required		(P)				
Ironpan Podzol		P	"		P				
Heathland podzol, ironpan and surface water gley		P	"	(N)P		N	NP	N	
Peaty gley Peaty ironpan Peaty podzol	shallow phase	P	"		P				P
	deep phase	P(K)	"		PK				PK
Deep peat	flushed	P(K)	"		PK				PK
	unflushed	(PK)	"		PK	N	N	N	NPK

( ) indicates possible benefits.

species requiring a different chemical at the next weeding.

The large number of weed and crop species and the variety of herbicides and application methods make the subject a complicated one. The reader is directed to Forestry Commission Field Book 8 *The use of herbicides in the forest* where detailed advice can be found. In practice it is likely that for any particular forest area a range of say three herbicides and application methods will cope with the various weeding situations encountered.

Fertilising

Forestry Commission Bulletin 95 *Forest fertilisation in Britain* deals comprehensively with this subject. Trees are generally well furnished with mycorrhizal roots, and are able to find adequate supplies of nutrients without the addition of artificial fertiliser, on all but the most demanding sites. The major exception to this is that Sitka spruce and lodgepole pine have been planted on some very demanding sites in the uplands deficient in all three macro-nutrients (nitrogen, phosphorus and potassium) and also some micro-nutrients, notably copper and magnesium.

Standard fertiliser regimes have been recommended for Sitka spruce (Table 5.6). Pines and larches are better able to obtain nitrogen than spruces, and it has been shown that Sitka spruce has greatly improved nitrogen nutrition when mixed with Japanese larch or lodgepole pine on difficult upland soils (e.g. iron poor soils, deep peats). Nitrogen deficiency in Sitka spruce, and the relative benefits of heather control and nitrogen fertiliser, are dealt with in detail in Forestry Commission Bulletin 89 *Nitrogen deficiency in Sitka spruce plantations*.

Although broadleaves have not been tested to the same extent as conifers, there is no evidence to suggest that additional growth responses are obtainable with fertilisers applied to broadleaves on the majority of sites on which they are planted, with the possible exception of nitrogen fertiliser in ash stands.

Cleaning

The cutting of unwanted woody growth may become necessary in a young plantation after weeding has ceased and the trees are properly established. Areas regenerated by direct sowing or natural regeneration almost always need to be cleaned to reduce stocking and at the same time remove unwanted species. A judgement always has to be made on the effectiveness of the operation relative to likely crop losses and the high cost of cleaning.

Brashing

This is the term applied to the removal of lower branches up to a height of about 2 m to facilitate access for thinning. Nowadays brashing, which is very labour intensive and costly, is not normally undertaken as a separate operation unless access for sporting is important, but is carried out at time of thinning at the minimum intensity needed for access.

Pruning

The removal of branches is undertaken to improve the quality of timber in the lower stem of the tree. The work should be done in stages when the stem is small in diameter so that subsequent growth produces a cylinder of knot-free timber around the knotty stem core.

In conifers only dead branches or exceptionally the lowest living whorl should be removed. Removal of more than one third of the green crown has been shown to cause a marked reduction in growth.

Pruning of conifers grown at conventional spacings for sawlog production is unlikely to be an economic proposition. Pruning is most justified on broadleaved trees capable of producing high value timber of veneer quality. Pruning should then be done to a height of 5–6 m over a limited time scale of 5–6 years. This will necessitate removal of live branches but in this case these are likely to contribute little to the economy of the tree. Furthermore in broadleaved trees there appears little difference in the susceptibility of green and dead pruning wounds to decay.

Thinning

The primary aim of thinning is the removal of a proportion of the growing trees in order to increase the diameter increment of the remainder, thus reducing the time for trees to reach the valuable sawlog size and increasing the proportion of sawlog material. When selective thinning is undertaken, deformed and unthrifty trees are removed thus allowing their growing space to be used by good quality trees.

Although thinning is a high cost operation it is usually undertaken with the aim of providing income. Poor markets for small roundwood may restrict thinning programmes. With broadleaves a rising demand for fuelwood has led to a revival of thinning. Selective thinning incurs the highest harvesting costs. In stands of reasonable form, line thinning can be carried out which simplifies harvesting but, as it is arbitrary in the removal of trees, it does not reduce the proportion of defective trees.

In a recently thinned stand the remaining trees have greater freedom of crown which means that movement in the wind is greater. Recently thinned crops are therefore vulnerable to windthrow and this is a serious risk in the uplands where soil types restrict rooting depth and the incidence of wind is greater than in the lowlands. The serious danger of windthrow following thinning operations has led to the adoption of 'no thin' regimes in some upland areas. Thinning regimes are dealt with in Chapter 11.

Coppice

Coppice is a crop raised from shoots produced from the cut stumps (called stools) of the previous crop. All broadleaves except for beech and certain alders can be worked in this way to produce small roundwood products, sticks, firewood, pulpwood, and fencing materials, on rotations of 6–30 years depending on species (Table 5.7). Except in the case of hazel, coppice can generally be resumed even after a period of 60 years neglect.

Coppicing has many wildlife and sporting benefits as well as being a low cost system of management. Unless some trees are grown among the coppice to large size (standards) no timber will be produced.

Table 5.7 Coppice practice

Species	Rotation years	No. of stools per hectare	Products
Sweet chestnut	15	800–1000	Stakes, fence paling, hop poles
Oak	30	600–800	Fuelwood, tan bark, charcoal
Other hardwoods and mixed coppices	20–25	600–1200	Fuelwood, pulpwood, turnery
Short rotations Mixed species	7–10	about 2000	Pea and bean sticks, hedge-laying stakes
Hazel	6–9	about 2000	Spars (thatching), hurdles

For many small lowland broadleaved woods (often known as coppices or copses) resumption of coppicing will be the simplest way of bringing them back into management and producing some worthwhile material.

Except for woodlands of less than 2 ha it is better to divide the whole area by the number of years in the coppice rotation and cut this amount each year. In this way a constant annual yield of produce is obtained. For very small woods it is probably best to coppice at intervals working at least 0.2 ha each time.

Coppice working

Stems are cut in the normal way using a chain saw, but extra care should be taken not to tear or damage the bark at the base of the stump below the point of cut. Cutting may be done at any time between August and April. Care must be taken in extracting the cut stems in order to prevent damage to the stumps (also called stools). Similarly if lop and top is burned on the site this must be done well away from any stumps.

It is generally not necessary to protect young coppice shoots against browsing damage since their growth is vigorous and the damage usually confined to peripheral shoots. Initially in the life of a coppice crop large numbers of shoots grow up but these rapidly thin themselves and no formal thinning is necessary.

At each coppicing a few stumps usually die and when this loss creates a large gap (more than 6 m across) it is necessary to establish a new tree for future coppicing. This may be done either by planting or by bending down to layer a shoot from a neighbouring stump which has been left especially for this purpose.

Coppice with standards

In many coppice woodlands trees are grown to timber size with the coppice as underwood. Such trees are called 'standards' and generally occupy 30% to 40% of the area. Their crowns must be far apart and never touching so as to allow plenty of light on to the coppice crop below. In a fully functioning coppice with standards system, the standards will consist of from three to six different age classes with the numbers of trees as shown in Table 5.8. Standards are almost always oak.

At each coppicing, trees in the oldest age class of standards are felled and a few new ones established.

Table 5.8 Traditional stocking for standards

	Age class/coppice rotation			
	1	2–3	3–4	4–6
Name of 'standard'	Teller	2nd class	1st class	Veteran
No. of stems per hectare	50	30	13	7
Maximum percentage of area occupied	10	10	10	10

Standards among coppice may either be planted, recruited from suitable natural regeneration or occasionally allowed to develop by encouraging one shoot on a coppice stool to develop into large size, a practice called 'storing coppice'.

Converting coppice to high forest

Many coppice woodlands in Britain are well past the normal age of cutting and are becoming a form of high forest. This process can be aided and the quality of the stand improved by removing all stems except the best one (straightest, most vigorous) on each stump. The operation is called 'singling' coppice and the stems grown on to large trees are known as 'stored coppice'. Once the operation is done the stand can be treated as a normal forest for thinning, felling and other operations.

APPENDIX: Notes on individual species

Most commonly used conifers

The figures quoted for the yield of various species are the range found in Britain, followed by the average in brackets. In an even-aged stand the cumulative volume production including dead trees and thinnings, divided by the age of the stand, is referred to as the mean annual increment (MAI). After planting, MAI increases during the early years of vigorous growth, reaches a maximum and then declines with increasing age. The point at which the MAI curve reaches a maximum is the maximum average rate of volume increment which a particular stand can achieve, and this indicates the yield class. For example a stand with a maximum MAI of 14 m^3 per hectare has a yield class of 14.

Scots pine
Pinus sylvestris L.
British Isles and northern Europe

Site
An adaptable tree which succeeds over a wide range of conditions. The easiest tree to establish on dry heather sites. Thrives on light or sandy soils and at low or moderate elevations. Very frost hardy, a strong light demander. Does well in low rainfall areas. A useful nurse species.

Avoid waterlogged ground and sites exposed to sea wind. Not easy to establish on moorland country under high rainfall. Unsuitable for chalk or limestone soils except as a nurse for beech. Not a tree for high elevations except in north-east Scotland where it grows at up to 450 m (1500 ft).

Timber
A general purpose timber with good strength properties. It works, nails and finishes well. Takes preservatives readily, so it is easily treated for outdoor use. Its wide range of uses includes fencing, joinery, building, flooring, box and packing case manufacture, railway sleepers, pitwood, fibreboard, woodwool and chipboard manufacture, and telegraph poles. The 'redwood' of the imported timber trade.

Yield
4–14 (8)

Remarks
Although growth is rather slow and volume production is not high compared with the more exacting species, generally this is a 'safe' tree to plant.

Corsican pine
Pinus nigra var. *maritima* (Ait.) Melville
Corsica

Site
Low elevations, particularly sandy areas near the sea. Light sandy soils but also heavy clays in the Midlands and south and east England; low rainfall areas. More successful on chalky soils than Scots pine. Tolerates smoke better than other evergreens.

Avoid high elevations. Not suitable for the northern and western uplands of Britain.

Timber
The timber resembles that of Scots pine but is coarser in texture, has a higher proportion of sap-

wood and has slightly lower strength properties. Readily treated with preservatives. Its uses include box manufacture, pitwood, fencing, fibreboard manufacture, pulpwood and woodwool. It is the preferred species for woodwool slab manufacture.

Yield

6–20 (11)

Remarks

It is important to obtain plants of true Corsican origin, that is plants raised from seed collected in Corsica or their descendants. Produces timber faster than Scots pine. More difficult to establish than Scots pine.

Lodgepole pine

Pinus contorta Dougl. ex Loud.
Western North America

Site

After suitable ground preparation lodgepole pine grows relatively well on the poorest heaths, sand-dunes and peat where no other tree will produce timber. It stands exposure better than most other species. Fairly tolerant of air pollution. For optimum results the choice of correct origin is important (see Forestry Commission Bulletin 66 *Choice of seed origins for the main forest species in Britain*). Tends to grow very coarsely on moist fertile sites.

Timber

Similar properties to Scots pine and can be used for the same purposes.

Yield

4–14 (7)

Remarks

Is probably the best pioneer species in Britain and has been widely planted especially in the west and north. Coastal provenances generally have higher yield than inland provenances but are of poorer form. Vulnerable to pine beauty moth in north Scotland.

European larch

Larix decidua Mill.
Mountains of central Europe.

Site

Site requirements are exacting. Does best on moist but well-drained moderately fertile loams. A strong light demander. A good nurse tree. Has some tolerance of air pollution.

Avoid damp, badly drained or very dry sites, frosty places, shallow soils over chalk, poor sands, peat soils, leached soils, exposed sites at high elevation or near the sea, areas carrying a dense growth of heather.

Timber

The timber is heavier and stronger than most other softwoods. The hardwood is naturally durable but any sapwood needs preservatives for outdoor use. It is widely used for fencing, gates and estate work. Other uses include telegraph poles, rustic work, garden furniture and chipboard. Selected material is in demand for vat making, boat building and wagons.

Yield

4–14 (7)

Remarks

Canker is a danger and it is essential to select suitable sites for planting. Choice of origin of seed for plants is most important. Home collected seed (particularly Scottish) from a good stand, is the most reliable. Seed from the high Alps (over 1100 m – 3500 ft) must be avoided. Sudeten and Polish provenances are promising. Not a high yield species.

Japanese larch

Larix kaempferi (Lamb.) Carr.
Japan

Site

Thrives over a wide range of conditions including the high rainfall districts of the west and north. Suitable for upland sites including grassy and heathery slopes. It quickly outgrows and suppresses adjoining vegetation. A valuable pioneer species and useful nurse with some resistance to air pollution.

Avoid dry sites and areas where the annual rainfall is low (under 750 mm – 30 in); also badly drained sites, frost hollows and very exposed situations.

Timber

The timber is strong and resembles that of European larch. Grade for grade, it can be used for the same purposes.

Yield

4–16 (8)

Remarks

Resistant to larch canker. Faster growing than European larch or Scots pine.

Hybrid larch

Larix × eurolepis Henry
First raised in Scotland.

Site

Of special value on sites which are at the limits for the use of European larch. Hardier and more resistant to disease. On good sites can grow even more quickly than Japanese larch. Shows some tolerance of smoke pollution.

Avoid dry sites and areas where annual rainfall is low (under 750 mm – 30 in); also badly drained sites, frost hollows and very exposed situations.

Timber

Resembles the timber of European larch and grade for grade can be used for much the same purposes.

Yield

4–16 (8)

Remarks

Characteristics are intermediate between European and Japanese larch. First generation hybrid from selected parents is outstanding. Second generation hybrid is also valuable. Work is going ahead on the vegetative propagation of selected superior clones.

Douglas fir

Pseudotsuga menziesii (Mirb.) Franco
Western North America

Site

Requires a well drained soil of good depth and of moderate fertility. A tree for valley slopes. Particular care is needed in site selection. A moderate shade bearer in its early years.

Unsuitable for exposed positions, heather ground, waterlogged and shallow soils. Liable to windthrow on soft wet ground except where drains are well maintained. Suffers from frost damage when young.

Timber

An excellent constructional timber with a high strength to weight ratio in compression and bending. Takes preservatives reasonably well. It is used for fencing, flooring, joinery, building, packing case manufacture, telegraph poles, flag poles, chipboard, fibreboard and pulpwood.

Yield

8–24 (14)

Remarks

On suitable sites Douglas fir grows rapidly and produces a high volume of timber. Delayed thinning can render the crop unduly susceptible to windthrow. Good drainage is important.

Norway spruce

Picea abies (L.) Karst.
Europe

Site

Moist grassy or rushy land and shallow, less acid peats. Succeeds on old woodland sites and most soils of moderate fertility including heavy clays. Can withstand light shade for a few years. Somewhat sensitive to exposure.

Fails on heather land and does poorly on dry sites particularly on the eastern side of Britain. May be checked by frost in hollows and by occasional grazing by deer and sheep but eventually grows away from this.

Timber

A good general purpose timber with a clean white colour. It works and nails well and has a wide range of uses. It is stable during changing conditions of humidity and is therefore particularly suitable for building. Its other uses include joinery, kitchen furniture, boxes and packing cases, pulpwood, chipboard, fencing, fibreboard, woodwool, ladder poles and scaffold poles. The 'whitewood' of the imported timber trade. Seldom used out of doors as the hardwood is difficult to treat with preservative but small poles take enough preservative in their sapwood to fit them for fencing.

Yield

6–22 (12)

Remarks

Norway spruce produces a high volume of timber. Good drainage is essential if windthrow is to be avoided. The young trees and often tops of thinnings can be sold as Christmas trees. Choice of origin is important. East European origins have grown well.

Sitka spruce

Picea sitchensis (Bong.) Carr.
Western North America

Site

Damp sites generally, including exposed high land. Stands exposure better than any other common conifer. Very suitable for high rainfall districts especially on the west coast.

Avoid all dry sites. Honey fungus is a risk in some

scrub and coppice areas. Not a tree for the dry east, nor for southern and midland England. Can suffer severe damage from spring frost when young.

Timber

Properties and usage are similar to those of Norway spruce. A first class pulpwood and readily accepted for chipboard, boxboards and many building jobs but not for high grade joinery.

Yield

6–24+ (12)

Remarks

A faster grower than Norway spruce and a very large volume producer. Wide origin variation. Queen Charlotte Islands (BC) is a safe choice but on southern sites Washington and Oregon are preferred.

Western hemlock

Tsuga heterophylla (Raf.) Sarg.
Western North America

Site

No well marked climate preferences. Does well in the west. May be highly productive in quite low rainfall areas. Acid mineral soils and the better peats. A strong shade bearer and excellent for underplanting. Most competitive with other shade bearers on dry brown earths. Rather difficult to establish pure on bare ground and does better with a nurse.

Dislikes heather competition and is slow to establish on heaths where it may eventually grow well. Sites where previous conifer crops have suffered from *Heterobasidion annosum (Fomes)* and *Armillaria mellea* should be avoided as hemlock is prone to butt rot from these fungi.

Timber

Home-grown hemlock has good prospects as a building timber and if graded for the purpose, as a joinery timber. Also for general estate work.

Yield

12–14+ (14)

Remarks

Is best established under some shade.

Western red cedar

Thuja plicata D. Don
North America

Site

Requires a sheltered site with a deep fertile, freely-drained soil. Does best in high rainfall areas of the south and west but has also performed satisfactorily on thin soils over chalk. Not too susceptible to frost. Shade tolerance and narrow crown shape make it useful in mixtures. Avoid very dry sites.

Timber

A very light timber with a coloured heartwood which is extremely durable. Can be used as sawn timber for framing in greenhouse, seed boxes, gates and cladding on buildings. Also used for chipboard and pulpwood.

Yield

6–24 (12)

Remarks

A useful estate tree with uses as fencing when young. Good in mixtures and useful cover for sporting woods. Especially good on alkaline soil. The best seed origin is the Olympic Mountains, Washington.

Principal broadleaves

Oaks

Pedunculate oak, *Quercus robur* L., and sessile oak, *Quercus petraea* (Matt.) Lieb.
British Isles and Europe

Site

Strong light demanders. Requiring well-aerated deep fertile loams, pedunculate oak grows well on fertile heavy soils and marls, sessile oak tolerates less rich soils.

Avoid all shallow, ill drained or infertile soils and exposed areas. It appears that timber is liable to 'shake' on very free draining soils.

Timber

Oak is hard and resistant to abrasion. It has a naturally durable heartwood but the sapwood needs preservative treatment when small poles are to be used out of doors. Prime clean oak is used for veneers, furniture, gates, flooring and barrel staves for tight cooperage. Lower grades of oak are used for fencing, weatherboarding, engineering, wagon construction and repair, sawn mining timber. Round oak is used for hardboard, pulpwood and chipboard. Small poles are valued for cleft or round stakes.

Yield

2–8 (4)

Remarks

Both species are very windfirm. Bark is still harvested as tanbark in southern England.

Beech

Fagus sylvatica L.
Southern England, south Wales and Europe

Site

Only tolerant of chalk and limestone soils provided free calcium carbonate is absent from surface layers. Good loams of all types if well drained. Likes a mild sunny climate. A good shade-bearer.

Avoid frost hollows, heavy soils on badly drained sites and leached soils. Avoid growing in treeshelters under shade.

Timber

Beech has a wider range of indoor uses than any other home-grown hardwood but is rarely employed out of doors. It is strong, works well to a good finish and is easily stained. Its uses include furniture, flooring, veneers, bentwood and pulpwood. It is a good wood for charcoal making and firewood.

Yield

4–10 (6)

Remarks

Benefits from a nurse on exposed areas. Scots pine is a suitable species. Useful for underplanting. Grey squirrels can be very destructive to young beech. Stem form often poor. Dense planting gives better chance of selecting individuals for final crop.

Ash

Fraxinus excelsior L.
British Isles and Europe

Site

For timber production this is an exacting species which requires good soil conditions especially rich in nitrogen. Grows best in sheltered situations and on deep calcareous loams, moist but well drained. Thrives on chalk and limestone but only where soil is reasonably deep. Benefits from shelter in youth. Not a suitable forestry species for large-scale planting or for use on open ground.

Avoid dry or shallow soils, grassland, heath or moorland, ill drained ground, heavy clays. Frost hollows and exposed situations are also unsuitable.

Timber

Ash has a resistance to shock and is thus used for hockey sticks and other sports equipment, tool handles and turnery in furniture, also for pulpwood.

Yield

4–10 (5)

Remarks

Planting ash for timber is risky unless there is local evidence that first-class trees can be produced. It is rare to find suitable conditions except in small patches and it is necessary to choose these sites with great care.

Sycamore

Acer pseudoplatanus L.
Central Europe

Site

Requires a moderately fertile freely drained soil. It is tolerant of calcareous soils. Fairly frost hardy. Stands exposure and smoke pollution very well. Not a suitable species for large-scale planting.

Avoid dry or shallow soils, heath or moorland, ill drained ground, heavy clays and frost hollows.

Timber

A white timber especially suitable for use in contact with food (kitchen utensils, butchers blocks, breadboards, etc). A good turnery timber used for textile rollers and bobbins. Suitable also for pulpwood. Figured sycamore is much sought after for veneer and furniture manufacture.

Yield

4–12 (5)

Remarks

A useful windfirm tree suitable for mixture with conifers in shelterbelts. Grey squirrels can be very harmful.

Sweet chestnut

Castanea sativa Mill.
Mediterranean

Site

Needs a moderately fertile light soil and it does best in a mild climate. Profitable as coppice in the south of England.

Unsuitable for frosty or exposed sites, badly drained ground or heavy clays.

Timber

Coppice-grown material is used for cleft fencing and hop poles. Sawn timber is used for furniture and coffin boards.

Yield

4–10 (6)

Remarks

When grown for timber there is a risk of shake.

Poplars: black hybrids

Populus × euramericana (Dode) Guinier
P. 'Eugenei', P. 'Gelrica', P. 'Heidemij', P. 'Robusta', P. 'Serotina'

Site

Very exacting; suitable sites are limited. Loamy soils in sheltered situations. Rich alluvial or fen soils, both well-drained and well-watered. Banks of streams.

Avoid high elevations, exposed sites and shallow soils. Stagnant water is fatal but occasional floods do no harm. Avoid acid peats and heathland. Not suitable for northern and western Britain.

Timber

Large clean poplar is peeled for veneer. Also used for light boxes and crates, packaging, pallets and fencing. High resistance to abrasion. Good pulp wood.

Yield

4–14 (6)

Remarks

Poplar growing is a specialised job and is dealt with in Forestry Commission Bulletin 92 *Poplars for wood production and amenity*.

Balsam poplars

P. tacamahaca × trichocarpa hybrids
North America

Site

Often susceptible to a bacterial canker and only clones generally resistant in practice should be used, e.g. *P. trichocarpa* 'Fritzi Pauley' and 'Scott Pauley' and the *P.* 'Balsam Spire' (T × T 32). They withstand slightly more acid soils than the black hybrids and are most suited to the cooler and wetter parts of Britain. Avoid high elevation, exposed sites and shallow soils. Stagnant water is fatal but occasional floods do no harm. Avoid acid peats and heathland.

Timber

Large clean Balsam poplar has similar uses to the black hybrids.

Yield

4–16 (6)

Remarks

Poplar growing is a specialised job and is dealt with in Forestry Commission Bulletin 92 *Poplars for wood production and amenity*.

Poplar clones acceptable for registration under the Forest Reproductive Material Regulations (1977)		
P. deltoides × nigra	'Robusta'	
P. deltoides × nigra	'Serotina'	
P. deltoides × nigra	'Eugenei'	
P. deltoides × nigra	'Gelrica'	
P. deltoides × nigra	'Heidemij'	
P. deltoides × nigra	'Casale 78'	(formerly I–78)
P. deltoides × nigra	'Primo'	
P. deltoides × nigra	'Ghoy'	
P. deltoides × nigra	'Gaver'	
P. deltoides × nigra	'Gibecq'	New poplar hybrids*
P. trichocarpa × deltoides	'Beaupré'	
P. trichocarpa × deltoides	'Boelare'	
P. × trichocarpa	'Fritzi Pauley'	
P. × trichocarpa	'Scott Pauley'	
P. tacamahaca × trichocarpa	'Balsam Spire '	(formerly T × T 32)
P. alba × tremula	P. × canescens	

*Six new poplar hybrids from Belgium have been added to the list of clones approved for commercial production in the UK. They are resistant to the major poplar diseases and have the potential to produce much higher yields than existing approved clones. Under certain circumstances they will qualify for grant aid but the planting of large blocks is not recommended until much more is known about their performance in the UK.

Wild cherry (gean)

Prunus avium L.
British Isles and central Europe

Site

Requires a fertile, deep, well-drained soil which ideally should be slightly acid although it also does well on deep loams over limestone. It responds well to chemical weeding and to early thinning and can be grown in the open. Avoid dry or shallow soils, ill drained ground and exposed situations.

Timber

Cherry timber has a rich reddish brown heartwood which is very rarely if ever shaken. It is suitable for turnery, furniture, veneers and decorative panelling.

Yield

4–10

Remarks

Best grown as groups in a mixture of broadleaves. Not often damaged by grey squirrels but suffers from bacterial canker and an aphid pest. It can produce very high value timber particularly if heavily thinned and high pruned.

Southern beech

Nothofagus procera (Poepp. and Endl.) Oerst., *N. obliqua* (Mirb.) Bl.
South America

Site

Requires a moderately fertile sheltered site. Will grow on most soil types apart from shallow soils over chalk or on acid peats. Will generally produce good volume growth on sites regarded as marginal for ash or oak.

Timber

Both species produce a moderately dense, fairly strong wood which may be used for furniture, flooring, interior and exterior finishes, firewood and pulpwood.

Yield

10–20 (12)

Remarks

Careful attention should be given to provenance as both species can suffer dieback and death as a result of extreme winter cold. The best stands in Britain have been raised from seed collection in the Chilean provinces of Cautin and Malleco, although recent provenance trials indicate that Argentinian seed lots can be markedly superior.

6 Diseases and disorders

This chapter briefly describes the principal infectious diseases in British forestry and gives control measures where appropriate. It also deals with those non-living causes of damage which do not warrant a chapter to themselves.

Damage caused by the two main groups of animal pests, the vertebrates (specifically mammals and birds) and the invertebrates (in this context, insects and some other arthropods), is considered in Chapters 8 'Wildlife management' and 7 'Insect pests'.

The avoidance and alleviation of damage to crops which can result from the chemical or physical nature of the soil (nutrient deficiencies, waterlogging, compaction) or from weed competition is discussed in Chapter 5 'Establishment and tending'. Fire is a serious threat to the survival of forests and its prevention, detection and control is discussed in Chapter 9 'Fire protection'. Damage due to poor cultural practices or the inappropriate use of chemicals such as herbicides is not discussed here. Guidance on good silvicultural practice can be found in Chapter 11 'Management for timber production'.

Damage in the nursery

Damage to nursery crops is only very briefly reviewed as this subject is dealt with in detail in *Nursery practice** (currently under revision).

The raising of forest planting stock involves many varied and potentially damaging mechanical and chemical operations. Furthermore, because of their small size, young plants, especially in their first few months of growth, are extremely sensitive to damaging agents, both biotic and abiotic, which on older trees may cause no obvious symptoms. The range of possible causes of damage to nursery plants is therefore large and their diagnosis can be difficult. This section, therefore, only draws attention to the commoner and more readily identifiable problems and in particular to those which are sufficiently common and serious to merit protective treatment.

More detailed, illustrated descriptions of the commonest forest nursery diseases which are tabulated below (Table 6.1), and the circumstances which favour their development, are given in Forestry Commission Bulletin 43 *Nursery practice** (under revision).

Damage in the forest

Infectious diseases

Infectious tree diseases are caused principally by fungi, less commonly by bacteria and viruses. The organisms responsible are often concealed within the tissues of the tree and manifest themselves (in the form of fruit bodies or mycelium or bacterial slime) erratically or only at a late stage of the disease. Furthermore, similar symptoms can be the result of widely differing causes, living and non-living. Few diseases, therefore, can be unequivocally diagnosed without detailed work. Unless the disease syndrome closely matches a description given below, the reader is advised not to institute any elaborate or expensive control measures without first consulting a tree pathologist.

In the ordering of this section, consideration is given first to diseases affecting a number of different

J.N. Gibbs, Principal Pathologist and **R.G. Strouts**, Advisory Pathologist

Table 6.1 Infectious diseases in the nursery. Susceptible crops, damage caused, contributory factors and control measures

Susceptible species	Disease or causal fungus	Effect	Circumstances favouring disease development	Control
Most species to some degree	Damping off	Germinating seed and young seedlings die.	Infested soil, growing medium or irrigation water. Wet soil.	Sterilise soil before sowing or use sterile medium. Purify water.
Most species	Grey mould (*Botrytis*)	Foliage and shoots die. Plants may die.	Crowded plants especially in greenhouses. Plants injured mechanically or chemically.	Avoid injury. Encourage rapid foliage drying after rain or irrigation by wide spacing. Apply fungicidal sprays immediately disease is seen.
Scots pine Corsican pine	*Lophodermium* needle cast	Foliage browning.	Proximity to older SP, CP plants or trees. Wet late summer.	Grow well away from pine plantations. Apply fungicidal sprays in summer.
European larch (hybrid larch)	*Meria* needle cast	Foliage browning but younger needles often escape infection.	Proximity to older larch plants or trees. Wet growing season.	Grow well away from other larches. Apply fungicidal sprays during growing season.
Western red cedar	*Keithia*	Foliage and shoots die. Plants may die.	Proximity to older WRC plants or trees (within several miles).	Grow remote from other WRC. Apply fungicidal sprays during growing season.
Oaks	Oak mildew	Foliage function impaired. Shoot dieback occurs.	Warm, dry weather.	Apply fungicidal sprays immediately disease is seen.
Silver firs Douglas fir Lawson .cypress Sweet chestnut Beech *Nothofagus*	*Phytophthora*	(May also cause damping off.) Root death causes plants to die.	Infested soil or irrigation water. Wet soil.	Sterilise soil before sowing or transplanting. Purify water.

host species. Diseases of one or two host species are then described, with diseases of conifers preceding diseases of broadleaves.

Honey fungus root killing and butt rot (Forestry Commission Bulletin 100 *Honey fungus* and Forestry Commission Leaflet 79 *Decay fungi in conifers*)

What has long been regarded as one fungus, *Armillaria mellea*, is now known to be a group of several *Armillaria* species, alike in general appearance and behaviour but differing in the range of tree species they attack and in their ability to cause death. It is now clear that one of these is very common in stumps and woody debris in soil, but is unable to infect healthy trees. Therefore honey fungus and toadstools are not a reliable indicator of disease. Diagnosis is dealt with in detail in Forestry Commission Bulletin 100.

In forests, although large conifers are occasionally killed, honey fungus killing is mainly a problem of trees in the first few years after planting on sites formerly occupied by a previous tree crop. The fungus is most commonly associated with the stumps of broadleaved trees but conifers may also harbour it. Resistance to killing increases with age but rot in the roots of older trees may cause windthrow. Decay in the stem, known as 'butt rot' does not develop much above ground level and so is of little economic significance.

The fungus grows through the soil from infected stumps in the form of blackish, shoelace-like strands called rhizomorphs. These infect the roots and stem bases of healthy trees. Infected trees can usually be identified by the presence of a whitish, tissue-thin sheet of mycelium sandwiched between the dead bark and the underlying wood. A copious flow of resin may occur from the base of infected conifers.

On the rare occasions when the fungus is so

Honey fungus toadstools.

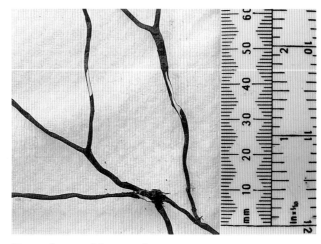
Honey fungus rhizomorphs.

damaging that it prevents the establishment of a new crop, a change to a more resistant species is the only control measure available. Of the common forest species, Douglas fir, the silver firs and broadleaves would be the best choice.

Honey fungus frequently invades the roots and stem bases of trees affected by other agents, so care should be taken not to attribute damage to this fungus merely because it is present.

Honey fungus root killing in Norway spruce.

Honey fungus butt rot in Norway spruce.

Fomes root and butt rot of conifers (Forestry Commission Leaflet 79 *Decay fungi in conifers*)

The fungus *Heterobasidion annosum* (formerly *Fomes annosus*) is the most serious cause of disease in British forestry and the only one against which routine control measures are widely applied. Economic losses are due chiefly to butt rot, which is most serious in the spruces, larches, western red cedar and western hemlock. However, in the first few years after planting, many species can be killed by the fungus. In Scots pine and Corsican pine deaths can continue throughout the life of the crop. Douglas fir and silver firs are fairly resistant to killing and butt rot, but may suffer windthrow as a result of root rot.

The decay caused by *H. annosum* is dry, stringy and fibrous. It is light brown with conspicuous white pockets. The fruit bodies of the fungus are perennial. They occur as brackets on stumps and at the base of killed trees, usually at soil level and often under fallen needles and vegetation. They are reddish-brown above with a conspicuous white margin when fresh. The underside is white and perforated by minute pores.

In first rotation crops, the fungus gains entry to the stand by means of airborne spores which infect freshly cut stump surfaces produced by thinning. The fungus colonises the stump and infects the roots of neighbouring trees through root contacts. In second rotation crops, infection occurs much earlier, having originated from stumps of the previous crop.

Stump infection may be prevented by the application of a chemical to the surface of all freshly cut stumps. In pine (but not in other species), prevention is better achieved by applying a suspension of the fungus *Peniophora gigantea*.

By preventing new stump infections, both treatments limit to some extent the build-up of disease in plantations which are already infected, and, in infected pines, *Peniophora* is especially valuable as it

Heterobasidion annosum fruit bodies.

Young Corsican pine trees killed by Fomes root rot.

85

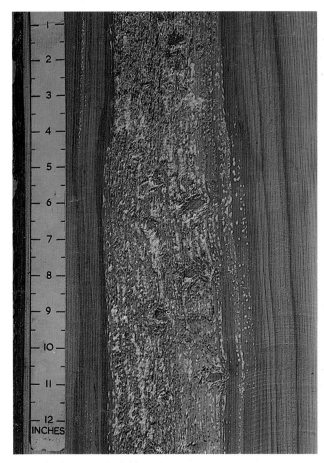

Fomes butt rot in European larch.

Phaeolus schweinitzii.

Phaeolus stem rot of conifers (Forestry Commission Leaflet 79 *Decay fungi in conifers*)

The fungus *Phaeolus schweinitzii* can cause a severe and extensive decay in standing trees. It is common on Sitka spruce, Douglas fir and the larches but is rarely a problem on other species. The disease is virtually confined to old woodland sites and at present is only significant locally.

Decayed wood is dry, brown and possesses a turpentine smell. It cracks radially and across the grain forming roughly cubical blocks. The fructifications are annual, appearing either as brackets at the tree base, or on the ground above infected roots, when they have a short central stalk. A fresh fully grown specimen is about 30 cm across and has a deep rusty-brown upper surface with a yellow margin. The underside is yellow-green and has angular irregular pores.

limits the volume of wood available to *H. annosum*. However, once a stand is infected, root-to-root infection will continue and the incidence of mortality and decay will increase. In certain circumstances, as in the sandy soils of the East Anglian pine forests, it may then eventually be both feasible and economically worthwhile to control the disease by destumping the site before replanting.

86

Phaeolus schweinitzii rot in Lebanon cedar.

The fungus persists in the soil and invades trees through roots which have been killed by honey fungus or, perhaps, in some other way. This connection with honey fungus may explain its link with old woodland sites. Quite young trees can be infected and some decay may be seen in thinnings. Infected trees remain alive but, with time, the decay becomes so severe that they snap a few feet from the ground. The only available means of control is to avoid the use of susceptible species on sites with a history of this disease.

Wound-associated stem decays and stains (Forestry Commission Leaflet 79 *Decay fungi in conifers,* and Arboricultural Leaflet 5 *Common decay fungi in broadleaves*)

The wood of any tree deprived of its protective covering of living bark is liable to invasion by bacteria, fungi, insects and other invertebrates. Whether this leads to significant timber degrade depends on a complicated interplay of factors among which the tree species and the size, location and character of the wound are of major importance.

Generally speaking, wounds which break wood fibres, such as those made during pruning, or by snow breakage, or gashes caused by timber extraction, are potentially much more harmful than those where the bark is cleanly removed as in the case of bark stripping by squirrels or damage by fire. However, certain species are so liable to stain or decay that even minor wounding can lead to considerable degrade.

Extraction damage is the principal cause of wound decay in conifers. Norway spruce is particularly liable to the problem. Losses are directly related to the size and incidence of wounds and are therefore readily minimised by skilful and careful felling and extraction.

Wounds which do not lead to decay and stain still constitute a defect in the timber and for some purposes, such as veneer cutting, will greatly reduce the value of timber and may even render it worthless.

Rhizina group dying of conifers

This root disease of pole-stage conifers is caused by the fungus *Rhizina undulata*. It is initiated by fire. Spores in the soil germinate at a temperature of 35–40°C and colonise the roots of fresh conifer stumps. From these the fungus is able to grow through the soil and kill healthy trees in a widening

Rhizina inflata fruit bodies.

circle. It also attacks newly planted trees following the burning of lop and top from a previous crop. The fruit bodies of the fungus, which are formed on the ground, are chestnut-brown cushion-like structures 4–12 cm across.

The fungus has a wide host range but Sitka spruce is particularly susceptible to the disease and groups of dead trees measuring up to 40 m across have been encountered. The host range also includes Norway spruce, Scots, Corsican and lodgepole pines and European and Japanese larch. Douglas fir appears to be very resistant, though killing of young plants has been noted abroad.

Most outbreaks can be traced to the sites of fires which have been lit inside plantations. The discouragement of this practice, and the reduction in the burning of lop and top, has relegated the disease to a rare curiosity. Control can be effected by trenching around groups while they are still small, although this is unlikely to be economically feasible.

Extensive Brunchorstia dieback in Corsican pine. In some cases the fungus has spread back and killed older wood.

Brunchorstia shoot killing of Corsican and Scots pine

In spring and early summer, the developing shoots of Corsican pine and Scots pine are susceptible to infection by spores of the fungus, *Gremmeniella abietina*. However, the fungus remains dormant in infected shoots and the onset of symptoms is delayed until the following late winter or spring when shoots are killed, causing the needles to turn brown

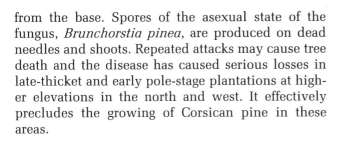

Gremmeniella abietina, the cause of Brunchorstia dieback on Corsican pine.

One-year-old lodgepole pine shoots killed by *Ramichloridium pini*.

from the base. Spores of the asexual state of the fungus, *Brunchorstia pinea*, are produced on dead needles and shoots. Repeated attacks may cause tree death and the disease has caused serious losses in late-thicket and early pole-stage plantations at higher elevations in the north and west. It effectively precludes the growing of Corsican pine in these areas.

Ramichloridium shoot killing of lodgepole pine

Although the symptoms of this disease were recognised in the late 1960s, the cause, the fungus *Ramichloridium pini*, was not identified until 1982. *R. pini* behaves on lodgepole pine in a similar way to *Gremmeniella abietina* on Corsican pine: spores produced on diseased tissues infect young developing shoots in early summer but symptoms do not appear until the following winter when diseased one-year-old shoots become conspicuous as the needles yellow, redden and die.

The disease occurs in all the lodgepole pine growing areas of the country in thicket and early pole-stage plantations and can kill enough shoots to cause the death of trees. More commonly, however, the disease results in the death of scattered shoots which has little effect on tree growth. Lodgepole pine provenances appear to vary considerably in susceptibility, Lulu Island being particularly liable to infection, and this provenance might be best avoided in new planting schemes.

Needle casts of pines

As well as being an occasional problem in the nursery, *Lophodermium seditiosum* can cause significant defoliation in Scots pine plantations. Current-year needles are infected in wet summers and these

One-year-old needles on Scots pine damaged and killed by *Lophodermium seditiosum*.

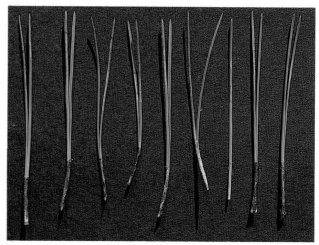

Lophodermella sulcigena on Corsican pine. Range of needle symptoms.

turn reddish-brown during the following winter and spring; the severity of the damage being positively related to the hardness of the winter. Previous attacks may have caused the loss of older needles so in extreme cases trees may be needle-less by early winter. Such trees may be attacked and killed by the pine shoot beetle, *Tomicus piniperda*. *Lophodermium* defoliation is sometimes a further element in the dieback caused by *Gremmeniella* (see above).

Corsican (rarely Scots) pine in the north and west of the country occasionally suffers conspicuous damage from *Lophodermella sulcigena*. This fungus infects the developing needles in July and by late October only the bases of needles remain alive. The dead tissue is at first pale brown, but damaged needles typically remain attached until the second autumn after infection, by which time they are grey in colour. Damage is rarely sufficiently serious to affect growth.

Phaeocryptopus needle cast of Douglas fir

In some seasons, Douglas fir plantations look very thin and drab yellow in colour. This is likely to be due to the infection of older needles by *Phaeocryptopus gäumannii*. Current year needles are infected in wet summers, and one to three years later these become yellow or brown and fall. No control measures are warranted.

Peridermium stem rust (resin top disease) of Scots pine

This sometimes fatal disease is prevalent only in parts of north-east Scotland, notably around the Moray Firth, and in East Anglia. The name 'resin top' comes from the resinous nature of the lesions on the trunk and major branches. The disease is not common on trees under 30 years of age. Corsican pine is only very rarely attacked.

The causal fungus, *Peridermium pini*, belongs to a

The spore stage of
Peridermium pini on a
Scots pine.

The top of a Scots pine
girdled and killed
by Peridermium stem rust.

Lophodermella sulcigena on Corsican pine.

group of exclusively parasitic fungi, the 'rusts'. Most infection occurs on young shoots but, by growing down through the bark of the branches, the fungus may eventually girdle the main stem causing dieback or death of the tree. Masses of bright orange spores are produced in early summer on the lesions and these are the agents of new infections. *P. pini* is an 'autoecious' species, so unlike many rusts requires no alternate host. Diseased trees are best salvaged at thinning.

Larch canker

This is a bark disease of European larch caused by the fungus *Lachnellula* (= *Trichoscyphella*) *willkommii*. Susceptibility is related to the origin of the larch, high Alpine provenances being the most susceptible and Carpathian, such as Sudeten larch, the least. Japanese larch is rarely attacked. Most hybrid larch are resistant but this depends on their parentage.

The perennating cankers usually begin around the base of a dwarf shoot or bud or around a wound. Each winter the fungus grows into the surrounding live bark killing a ring of tissue. In summer some callusing occurs at the canker margins but, slowly, the dead bark patch increases in size and may eventually girdle and kill the tree, branch or stem. The resultant flattened or sunken, resinous cankered areas often bear fruit bodies of the fungus. These are tiny, saucer-shaped structures, apricot orange to buff in colour with a white rim.

The disease can cause severe damage and even deaths in plantations of susceptible provenances of European larch, but a much more damaging type of dieback follows severe infestations by the insect *Adelges laricis*, whether canker is present or not (see Chapter 7 'Insect pests'). As high Alpine provenances are those most susceptible to this dieback as well as to the canker, the two disorders often occur together.

Larch canker – *Lachnellula willkommii.*

Beech bark disease (Forestry Commission Bulletin 69 *Beech bark disease*)

This disease may cause significant mortality and growth reduction in plantations between about 20 and 40 years of age, but seems to be no threat to the production of a final crop.

It develops where bark infested by an insect, the felted beech coccus (see Chapter 7) is subsequently invaded and killed by the fungus *Nectria coccinea*. The earliest signs of infection are small tarry spots and the exudation of a blackish liquid. Later, large numbers of minute, globular, red fruit bodies of the fungus develop on the dead bark. Small lesions may callus over, permitting lightly infected trees to recover. Often, however, trees are girdled and die, or decay fungi quickly invade surviving trees through the dead bark causing stem snap.

Prompt felling of affected trees is required if their timber is to be utilised. Stems heavily infested with the insect are best removed at thinning, as even

before the onset of disease their growth rate will be severely retarded. Other factors, such as severe drought, may predispose beech bark to attack by *N. coccinea* and then the same train of events is initiated.

Beech bark disease. Tarry exudations from dying bark, staining a heavy cover of the felted beech coccus.

Bacterial canker on balsam poplar trunk.

Bacterial canker on a 3 m high poplar.

Bacterial canker of poplar

This, the most damaging disease of poplars in Great Britain, is caused by *Xanthomonas populi*. Cankers are formed on branches causing dieback, while cankers on trunks render them useless for veneer cutting.

The bacteria ooze out of infected bark in moist, mild conditions and are distributed by rain, wind and insects. Most infections take place through wounds left by the shedding of bud scales in spring. Shoots or twigs may be girdled and killed and the bacterium may spread back into the older parts of the tree to cause a perennial canker.

Healthy stands can be protected to a large extent if cankered trees in the immediate vicinity are removed. However, long-term freedom from the disease can be achieved only by the use of resistant poplar varieties. Planting grants are available only for such approved varieties and these are listed in Forestry Commission Bulletin 92 *Poplars for wood production and amenity*.

Dutch elm disease

This disease is caused by the fungus *Ophiostoma (Ceratocystis) ulmi,* which invades the xylem vessels of the current annual ring. Extensive wilting of foliage results and an infected tree may die within a few weeks. The presence of staining in the outermost xylem of a diseased branch is a key diagnostic feature. The fungus is spread by elm bark beetles of the genus *Scolytus*, which breed in the bark of dying or freshly felled trees. Infection occurs when newly emerged adults, carrying spores of the fungus in and on their bodies, feed on the twigs of healthy trees. Local transmission of the fungus can also occur via the roots where trees have grafted together or, in the case of certain types of elm, have arisen as suckers on a common root system.

Control programmes against the disease rely upon

rigorous 'sanitation' felling to reduce the number of dying trees in which the beetles breed, but there are few woodland areas where such programmes are feasible. However, a number of factors have together resulted in a slower rate of disease increase in the woodland elm of north and west Britain than was the case in the English elm hedgerows of the south and east. These include the somewhat higher field resistance of the wych elm compared with English elm, and a series of natural constraints on the breeding and flight of the bark beetles.

In parts of southern Britain through which the disease has passed, vigorous regrowth of English elm is occurring from root suckers. This can offer a relatively cheap means of regenerating a woodland, but it must be recognised that the young trees are genetically identical to their predecessors and are vulnerable to new waves of infection.

Phytophthora root killing (ink disease) of sweet chestnut (Arboricultural Leaflet 8 *Phytophthora diseases of trees and shrubs*)

Soil-borne species of the fungus *Phytophthora* are the cause of many serious tree diseases throughout the world, but in British forests only ink disease of sweet chestnut is of any importance.

The presence of the fungus only becomes apparent when coppice stools or trees start to die. The fungus produces no visible fruit bodies or mycelium and it is the absence of any such sign of fungal attack on the dead and otherwise undamaged roots of dying trees which signals the likelihood that *Phytophthora* is responsible. The killed roots and the soil around them may turn an inky blue-black, hence 'ink disease', although this is a characteristic rather of dead sweet chestnut roots than of *Phytophthora* infection. The fungus often spreads up from the roots to kill tongue-shaped patches of bark on the lower stem – a valuable diagnostic feature.

The fungus requires free water for its development and spread, so outbreaks arise after wet periods and are commonest on water retentive sites. Diseased trees and stools may die quickly, or succumb to repeated attacks over a number of years, or recover. Improved drainage should ameliorate the problem but no other control measures are available. Severe and persistent outbreaks can be dealt with only by a change of species. Beech and Lawson cypress should be avoided since both are very susceptible.

Phytophthora disease on sweet chestnut. Notice the sharp delineation between dead and live tissue. Spread of the pathogen has ceased here.

Dutch elm disease: typical damage on a large English elm.

Abiotic diseases

Wind

In British upland forestry, wind is both a major cause of damage and a factor which strongly influences silvicultural practice. Means of anticipating and limiting its potential impact are discussed in Chapter 10. Salt-laden gales from the sea at any time of year can cause conspicuous, markedly directional browning of foliage. Salt deposited in this way in winter on deciduous trees can kill buds and twigs.

Winter cold

In winter, persistent cold winds may desiccate and kill twigs and evergreen foliage, particularly that on the windward side of the trees and branches. Freezing temperatures, especially if these occur before trees are fully hardened in winter or if they alternate with periods of very mild weather, can cause similar, though non-directional damage. Snow and ice can cause considerable damage by breaking branches and stems.

Extremely low winter temperatures, below −15°C, preclude planting of exotic species such as *Nothofagus*, *Pinus radiata*, *P. muricata* and eucalypts.

Spring frost

Spring frosts (often termed 'late frosts') can kill newly developing leaves and shoots and sometimes older tissues, and can severely retard establishment on frost-prone sites. If bare soil conditions can be maintained round the plants for one or two years this may be sufficient to allow them to grow through the frosty zone. Susceptible species include ash, beech, and oak among the broadleaves and Sitka spruce and grand fir among the conifers. Birch and Scots pine are resistant.

Autumn frost

Autumn or 'early' frosts can damage young unhardened tissue. On conifers such as Sitka spruce a common symptom is the browning of needles near the terminal bud.

Spring frost damage of newly flushed Norway spruce shoots.

Drought

Drought may merely cause temporary wilting or the shedding of older leaves or needles, but if it is prolonged, trees will die back or even die. Birch and larch are very susceptible to drought. Oak is resistant. The stems of some fast growing conifers, notably *Abies* spp., may crack longitudinally and, in severe cases, the timber from such trees may fall apart along the cracks when sawn.

Sun scorch

In woodland in southern Britain, bark on the south facing sides of previously shaded stems of thin barked species such as beech may be killed if these are suddenly exposed to the full heat of the sun by, for example, heavy thinning.

Flooding

During the dormant season, even prolonged periods of flooding (waterlogging) of roots are unlikely to be damaging unless the water is saline. During the growing season, however, trees are likely to die back if flooded for more than a week or two.

Lightning

In woodlands, whole groups of trees may be killed by lightning strike. Unlike the situation with solitary trees there is often little physical evidence of injury. Diagnosis rests largely on the suddenness of the damage, on the absence of other causes of injury and on the continued healthy condition of the roots some time after the crown has deteriorated.

Top dying of Norway spruce

One particular non-infectious disease merits a specific description because it can cause considerable losses in Norway spruce. Top dying is a common, non infectious disease of pole-stage and older (occasionally younger) crops. It seems to be a physiological problem which is related to the susceptibility of this species to exposure and water stress. Although the precise cause is not known, the circumstances leading to its development are clear. In mild, windy winters, susceptible individuals in pole-stage stands are affected by needle browning. This proceeds backwards from the shoot tip and may be slight or may affect the entire crown. Affected trees usually flush satisfactorily in spring but height and radial increment is reduced during the following growing season. Repeated browning leads to dieback and death. The condition typically affects scattered groups of trees throughout stands but is usually most severe on plantation edges. Damage is particularly common in narrow shelterbelts and frequently coincides with brashing, thinning or with the felling of adjacent plantations. This emphasises the likely importance of air movement in the development of this syndrome. Browning is particularly severe in dry years and may begin as early as late summer. Top dying occurs throughout Britain but is more common in the east than the west.

The management of affected plantations is difficult since salvage thinning increases air movement and may exacerbate the problem. Losses can be sufficiently high to necessitate premature clear felling.

Air pollution, acid rain and forest health

It has long been known that air pollution can cause significant damage to trees in Britain. The role of high levels of sulphur dioxide in preventing the establishment of conifer plantations on the Pennines during the 1950s and 1960s is well documented and, over the years, there have been many records of severe injury to trees near to sources of pollution. In 1984 surveys of tree health were initiated by the

Forestry Commission in response to a concern that low levels of air pollution might be damaging trees over wide areas. Since 1984, the survey has gradually been expanded and now includes 5 species (Sitka spruce, Norway spruce, Scots pine, oak and beech) on a total of 310 sites. Detailed assessments are made of 24 trees at each site with the main assessment being one of crown density. The most widely quoted index of tree health is crown density. This is a measure of the amount of light passing through the crown. It is not specific to damage by air pollution and should not be interpreted as such. For example, the architecture of the branches plays a major part in determining the crown density, as does the rate of growth. In some studies, a certain level of crown density reduction (e.g. 25%) is taken as a threshold for damage. However, there is no empirical justification for this; it appears the trees can lose more than 25% of their foliage without any effect on increment.

The surveys have indicated that many trees in Britain have thin crowns. This has been attributed to a variety of factors with climate being singled out as one of the most important. Insects and fungi also play a role. The time series that is available is insufficient to determine whether or not there have been any long-term changes in crown density. However, there is an increasing amount of evidence to suggest that thin-crowned trees have always been present and that no novel phenomenon has occurred in Britain in recent years.

In 1987 the European Community passed legislation making a systematic survey of tree health compulsory in all Member States. In the United Kingdom there are 75 sites involved in this survey, with approximately 1800 trees being assessed annually. The small sample size limits the value of this survey and the Forestry Commission places very little emphasis on it. However, it is the results of this survey that tend to be reported in the press and elsewhere.

A feature of the European reports is the apparent ill-health of British trees compared with those in other countries. However, it is now clear that such comparisons are invalid. There are major differences in the techniques used to assess trees in different countries. Britain uses particularly rigorous standards and makes no allowance for the growing environment of the tree. Those countries that use the same assessment system as Britain have very similar figures for crown density. As with the main monitoring programme, the surveys have not been conducted long enough to establish whether or not a long-term decline in tree health is occurring.

Analysis of the results of both surveys have failed to establish any clear relationships between the patterns of air pollution and patterns of ill-health in trees. If anything, the reverse has been found with trees appearing to be in better condition in areas with higher levels of pollution. A variety of explanations are available for this, although the most likely is that the environmental conditions in the south and east of England are such that they favour dense-crowned trees. (Forestry Commission Bulletin 88 *Monitoring of forest condition in the United Kingdom 1988*; Forestry Commission Bulletin 94 *Monitoring of forest condition in Great Britain 1989*; Forestry Commission Bulletin 98 *Monitoring of forest condition in Great Britain 1990*.)

7   Insect pests

British forestry has been subject to major changes during the 20th century, resulting in an extensive exotic tree flora in plantations which are composed mainly of conifers. In particular, afforestation using Sitka spruce has dramatically increased since the 1930s. However, despite these major changes there have been relatively few serious problems arising from the activities of insects.

This is somewhat surprising considering that the number of different insect species on our trees is large. For example oak and willow support between them over 450 species of insect. Even the conifers, which generally carry fewer species than broadleaves, are remarkably rich in insect herbivores; pine (more than 170 species) and spruce (90 species), having the greatest number of associated insect species, could, therefore, be regarded as being at greatest risk from attack.

There are a number of possible reasons why this large diversity of insect species remains mainly innocuous. Among these are the actions of natural enemies, the planting of trees suited to particular sites, the avoidance of forestry practices that could encourage insect outbreaks, particularly of bark beetles, and the fact that the bulk of our current tree cover, especially of conifers, is relatively recent, the implication being that problems have not yet had the opportunity to build up. It is not possible to determine which of these factors, alone or in combination, are most important in keeping insect pest numbers low. Indeed, the question of whether second, and later, crop rotations are likely to be more at risk remains to be answered.

In the account that follows it has been convenient to divide the examples of the more important insects according to the age of the crop. Further information may be found in Forestry Commission Handbook 1 *Forest insects*.

Insects attacking tree seed

Many insects live in the developing seeds and cones of forest trees and their attacks can sometimes result in appreciable losses. One particularly damaging species is the chalcid seed wasp *Megastigmus spermotrophus* whose larvae hollow out the seeds of Douglas fir. Infestations by this insect are sometimes very heavy and can cause near total loss of the seed crop, although this tends to occur only in poor seed years when a large proportion of the already low seed numbers can be infested. It is therefore advisable to make an assessment of the seed to determine its soundness before cone collecting is carried out. Other species of *Megastigmus* infest silver fir, larch and Norway spruce seeds.

The caterpillars of a number of moth species such as *Dioryctria abietella*, *Cydia strobilella* and *C. conicolana*; the larvae of the weevil *Pissodes validirostris*, and the maggots of some dipterous (two winged) flies, feed upon and destroy the seeds of various conifers. Their attacks, however, are not often serious. The knopper gall wasp *Andricus quercuscalicis* can destroy large numbers of acorns by transforming them into galls. The grubs of weevils of the genus

J.T. Stoakley, former Entomologist (North), and **H.F. Evans**, Principal Entomologist

Curculio attack and hollow out acorns, while beech nuts are similarly infested by the caterpillars of the moth *Cydia fagiglandana*. Again the attacks are not usually of a serious nature, but they may on some occasions affect the success of natural regeneration schemes or the economics of seed collection.

Other types of insect infestation can produce an indirect effect on seed production. For example the defoliation of oak by the oak leaf roller moth *Tortrix viridana* or of the winter moth *Operophtera brumata* may result in marked reduction in acorn yield.

Nursery pests

The most important nursery pests are soil inhabiting insects and sap suckers. Leaf eating insects are not usually troublesome in the nursery, but occasionally some moth and sawfly caterpillars and species of leaf beetle damage broadleaved stock. These pests can easily be controlled with insecticides applied at the rates recommended in normal horticultural practice.

Cutworms and chafer grubs

Two important groups of soil insects are cutworms and chafer grubs. Cutworms are the caterpillars of various species of noctuid moths which remain in the soil during daytime and emerge at night to feed upon the seedlings. The damage consists of gnawing at the root collar region, usually resulting in the young tree being girdled or cut off at or about soil level. When damage is detected the identity of the pest can be confirmed by digging up the caterpillars or looking for them on the surface of the soil at night with the aid of a torch. The caterpillars are dirty grey-green in colour and measure about 25 mm in length; their reaction to handling or disturbance is to roll themselves up into a coil. Another check on the identity of the pest is the presence of holes – the

entrance to the burrows – in the surface of the seedbed. A practical control can be achieved by using gamma HCH applied to the seedbed.

Chafer grubs are white, curved and wrinkled and measure up to 40 mm in length when full grown. They are the larvae of various species of scarabaeid beetles of which the best known is the large May bug *Melolontha melolontha*. A smaller species, *Serica brunnea*, is common in the north. The grubs live in the soil for 1 to 4 years and during this period feed on the roots of seedlings and transplants. The roots are either stripped of bark or chewed through. The first obvious symptom of attack is browning of the foliage, and the death of the plant is a common result of attack. Chafer grubs used to be the most important pests in old agricultural-soil nurseries, but with the change to the heathland type and with annual cultivation they do not appear to be so troublesome.

Springtails

The collembolan (springtail) *Bourletiella hortensis*, another soil dweller, can cause heavy losses among conifer seedlings. The attack takes place on the apical points of the hypocotyl and on cotyledons. Death of the seedlings can occur before emergence from the soil or, when damage has not been great, the shoot and needles may be deformed. At the end of the growing season the surviving plant has a normal stem (often showing brown specks of dead tissue), on top of which is a bush of swollen distorted needles. After a second year's growth the small trees appear perfectly green and healthy but bear four or five leaders – the kind of plant which will normally be rejected by the nurseryman. It is possible that collembolan damage on a small scale may be quite common and could account in part for the wide differences between laboratory-determined germination percentage and survival in the field.

Sap sucking insects

Aphids and adelgids are fairly common in nurseries, and their attacks may check and stunt the growth of plants. Adelgids are restricted to coniferous trees and their presence can be detected by the patches of white wool which they produce to cover themselves. *Pineus pini* on Scots pine, *Adegles cooleyi* on Douglas fir, *A. abietis* on spruce and *A. laricis* on larch are perhaps the most common and sometimes damaging. *Cinara pilicornis* feeds on the new shoots of spruce and sometimes causes local needle loss and a degree of distortion. *Phyllaphis fagi* on beech and *Myzus cerasi* on cherry are also often found feeding on the leaves of their hosts and bring about leaf curl and stunted growth. Another interesting aphid species, *Stagona pini*, may be found on the roots of pine in nurseries and is often associated with poor and dry conditions of growth; plants grown in clay pots tend to be particularly prone to infestation by this species. Most of the aphid species are controlled by the use of suitable approved insecticides such as are used to combat the attacks of green or black fly in gardens. In the case of adelgid species, however, which protect themselves under wool and have spring and summer egg stages, some difficulty may be experienced in reducing damage to an acceptable level. Careful timing of treatment and a suitable prevailing temperature are critical factors in adelgid control; a warm period in late autumn, winter or early spring provides optimum conditions for spraying.

The conifer spinning mite *Oligonychus ununguis* can be a serious pest of young conifers, particularly the spruces, in rather dry growing conditions. This tiny relation of the spiders sucks the sap from the needles causing them to turn a dirty brown colour and leaving them netted with fine silk. Good control can be obtained by using an approved acaricide.

Occasionally small weevils such as those in the genera *Otiorhynchus*, *Phyllobius* and *Barypithes* cause damage in the nursery by feeding upon roots, leaves and stems.

Insect attacks in young woods

Root and bark feeders

Generally speaking the first few years in the growth of a conifer crop are much more critical from the point of view of insect damage than in the same period in the life of a broadleaved stand. This is particularly true when the new conifer crop is a replacement for another one recently removed. In such a case, pests which have multiplied in the stumps and roots of the previous crop emerge to feed upon the young trees and may bring about heavy mortality if no protective measures are taken. The insects concerned in such situations are the so-called large pine weevil *Hylobius abietis* and the equally misnamed black pine beetles *Hylastes* spp. (Forestry Commission Leaflet 58*).

Hylobius abietis breeds in conifer stumps and roots. The grubs, which burrow beneath the bark of the roots and stump buttresses, measure 2 cm in length when full grown and are white, curved and legless. Development from egg to emergence of young adults takes between 1 and 2 years, depending on local climatic conditions. In particularly cold sites it may even take longer than this. On emergence the weevils, which can live in the adult stage for two or occasionally more years, cause damage when they feed by gnawing the bark of newly planted conifers above soil level. They may also feed on young broadleaved trees and on other plants. When the stem bark of young transplants is ringed the tree dies. Total loss of the crop is not an uncommon result of neglect to carry out protective measures. All of the commonly grown conifers appear to be susceptible to attack by this weevil.

Hylastes beetles also breed in conifer stumps and later emerge to attack young coniferous trees. Damage is caused by these small bark beetles burrowing beneath the bark at and below the root collar region of the young tree. The attack frequently causes the death of trees through girdling. Symptoms of attack are externally not so obvious as that by *H. abietis*, but it is an easy matter carefully to lift and examine obviously unhealthy and dying trees to determine if *Hylastes* is responsible. Serious outbreaks occur in many restocking areas and may be a particular problem where fellings take place in contiguous coupes.

The clay-coloured weevil *Otiorhynchus singularis*, like *Hylobius abietis*, can also bring about serious loss in new plantings. The larvae feed on the fine roots of various herbs and the adults upon the aerial parts of the forest trees and other plants. Western

hemlock seems particularly prone to attack. The adults not only eat triangular chunks from the needles, but also remove the bark from the finer twigs and branches in a manner similar to that of *H. abietis* feeding on the main stem. The creatures are dormant during the daytime but may be found just under the soil surface at the base of the stem. Adult activity usually starts at the end of April or early May and continues throughout the summer months into September. Almost identical damage, particularly to larch, is sometimes caused by the small brown weevil *Strophosomus melanogrammus*. Indeed these two are very often found in similar circumstances.

CONTROL MEASURES

Bare-rooted planting stock may be protected against *Hylobius abietis* and *Hylastes* spp. either by dipping the tops of the plants and the upper parts of their root systems in a solution of a suitable insecticide before planting or by spraying shortly after planting. Containerised stock may be drenched before planting or sprayed post-planting. In all cases 'top-up' spraying may be necessary during the first 2, possibly 3, years after planting. Appropriate treatments are mostly covered by 'Off-label' Approvals given under the Control of Pesticides Regulations 1986 and specify conditions of use and required safety precautions in some detail. Since these Approvals are short-term, intending users should refer to current Research Information Notes on the subject, published by the Forestry Commission, or seek advice from the Commission's Entomology Branch.

Hylobius abietis the large pine weevil.

Defoliators

In the first decade after establishment a number of insect pests make their presence felt, especially in coniferous crops. The sap sucking adelgids (Forestry Commission Bulletin 42* and Forestry Commission Leaflet 7*) are sometimes conspicuous on Douglas fir, the larches and the spruces. Although such attacks can be demonstrated to bring about a reduction in growth it is seldom economically worthwhile to attempt control artificially. One species, however, *Adelges nordmannianae*, so severely cripples the common silver fir *Abies alba* that the planting of this tree has seldom been attempted on a forest scale in this country (Forestry Commission Bulletin 26*). The so-called pineapple gall forming species *A. abietis* is a noteworthy pest of Norway spruce grown as Christmas trees.

Two species of pine sawfly, *Diprion pini* and *Neodiprion sertifer*, may cause significant damage on young pines (Forestry Commission Leaflet 35*). That due to *D. pini* is sporadic and small scale while outbreaks of *N. sertifer* may be extensive and severe,

Damage to young Scots pine due to *Hylastes ater*.

Neodiprion sertifer on lodgepole pine.

most notably in northern Scotland but also on other rather poor sites throughout Britain. Defoliation seldom brings about death of the tree although there may be a noticeable decrease in height increment. Outbreaks seldom persist for more than two or three seasons before they collapse naturally, through parasites in the case of *D. pini* and a nuclear polyhedrosis virus (NPV) in *N. sertifer*. Artificial dissemination of the virus gives efficient and worthwhile control of *N. sertifer*. A preparation of the virus is marketed as Virox by Oxford Virology Ltd. Extensive testing of this virus for both efficacy and environmental safety has been carried out by scientists at the NERC Institute of Virology and Environmental Microbiology and by Forestry Commission entomologists. It can be applied from the ground using most forms of insecticide sprayers (except thermal foggers) but for large-scale operations ultra low volume application from the air at one litre per hectare is the most practical method. Full instructions for application are supplied with the preparation. The aim is to spray larvae soon after hatch (normally around mid to late May) thus reducing damage to the trees to a minimum. Maximum impact is achieved if populations can be sprayed during the first or second year of infestation so that, having killed the relatively low population present, enough virus persists from the virus-killed larvae to exert control for at least 2 years.

In broadleaved crops of up to 10 years of age, defoliation by leaf beetles and by the caterpillars of moths and sawflies is sometimes encountered. Serious damage is rare and recovery is normally very good. Exceptions to this rule are the attacks made by the leaf beetles *Phyllodecta vitellinae* and *P. vulgatissima* on poplar stool beds. In the interests of increasing productivity of propagating material, insecticidal control may be necessary. Aphid attacks, too, may occur, but again they do not seriously interfere with the growth of crops.

Insects in older woods

Many species of leaf feeding insects cause damage of varying degrees of severity in older woods of all types. Some of the most harmful forest pests are included in this group and although crops in Britain have, by comparison with similar ones in other countries, remained fairly free from serious outbreaks in the past, it is essential to appreciate that some species have by no means yet reached their full potential as pests. The list of insects having achieved pest status has grown as the forest estate has increased in size, and the crops have become older. Since 1953, at least two species on spruce and three each on pine and larch have, without obvious reasons, found conditions ecologically suitable for outbreak. It is wise to remember, therefore, that we are still very much a developing country as far as plantation forestry is concerned, and our quickly expanding, largely exotic, forest holdings must still be considered vulnerable to ecological change and to chance import.

Defoliators

The most important forest defoliators in older crops are the caterpillars of moths and sawflies, but some examples also occur in groups other than these. For instance, beech leaves are often damaged by the weevil *Rhynchaenus fagi*, the adults of which eat holes in the leaves while the larvae mine the interior of the leaf.

Sitka spruce is frequently defoliated by the aphid *Elatobium abietinum*, and, although recovery from attack is normally good unless site conditions are particularly adverse, considerable loss of increment may result from severe defoliation. Outbreaks are invariably associated with mild winters, $-8°C$ being a threshold low temperature for winter survival (Forestry Commission Forest Record 84*). Control

Needle discoloration due to *Elatobium abietinum*.

measures against this aphid have never, in fact, been recommended, partly due to difficulties of forecasting severe attack, and thus of taking timely action, partly for the doubtful economics of such action, and partly for ecological objections to wholesale insecticide applications. In the nursery and in research plots good control can be achieved.

Adelges laricis is now recognised as not only responsible for wholesale canopy discoloration and degrade, but may also be the prime factor in bringing about the condition known for many years as 'dieback of European larch'. Alpine provenances of larch are found to be particularly susceptible to this malaise, while Carpathian provenances and hybrid larches are less so, and the Japanese larch is virtually resistant. The grey aphid-like creature may easily be spotted on the needles of larch often accompanied by white waxy wool. This, together with the honeydew produced by the aphid, blackened by sooty mould, is often conspicuous, and causes the foliage to appear a bluish-green by midsummer.

Elatobium abietinum on Sitka spruce. Recovery after complete defoliation.

Examples of moths causing defoliation are the pine looper *Bupalus piniaria* (Forestry Commission Leaflet 32*): the larch bud moth *Zeiraphera diniana* on pine, spruce and less commonly larch; the larch casebearer *Coleophora laricella*, on larch; the winter

107

Larva of *Panolis flammea*.

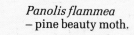

Panolis flammea
– pine beauty moth.

moth *Operophtera brumata* on oak, many other broadleaved trees and the spruces; and the oak leaf roller moth *Tortrix viridana* (Forestry Commission Leaflet 10*). The pine beauty moth *Panolis flammea* (Forestry Commission Record 120*), though long known as a pest on the continent, reached infestation level for the first time in 1976 on lodgepole pine in the north of Scotland. Outbreaks have since led to

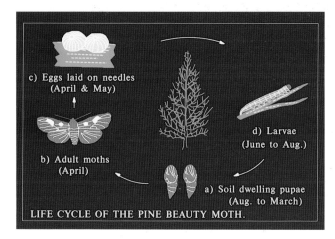

c) Eggs laid on needles
(April & May)

b) Adult moths
(April)

d) Larvae
(June to Aug.)

a) Soil dwelling pupae
(Aug. to March)

LIFE CYCLE OF THE PINE BEAUTY MOTH.

Life-cycle of *Panolis*.

severe defoliation and death of trees. The organophosphorus insecticide fenitrothion, and diflubenzuron, which interferes with formation of chitin in larvae, applied by aircraft, have both given satisfactory control – generally about 98% mortality. Fenitrothion was chosen for good contact action against larvae and low toxicity to mammals and fish. Diflubenzuron has to be ingested by larvae and has no action against adult invertebrates including beneficial insects. A virus has been isolated from dead larvae and its use as a suitable pathogen is being investigated with the aim of ultimately obtaining biological control of the insect.

The sawflies on pine have already been mentioned as has the fact that their attacks occur usually in young stands. Larch and spruce also carry a varied sawfly fauna with seven species occurring on the former tree and eight on the latter. These species on larch and spruce are of particular interest since they must all be foreigners to Britain, all being specific to exotic tree hosts.

Space allows only brief reference to the forest status of the above insects. Most of them occur in some numbers in woodlands containing their host tree but will indicate their presence through visible damage in restricted areas only. The winter moth and oak leaf roller moth are well known pests which periodically cause damage to older oak woods. The trees usually recover fairly well, assisted by heavy lammas shoot production, but a distinct loss of timber increment results. It is interesting to note that the later flushing sessile oak is less susceptible to heavy infestation than is pedunculate oak. The pine looper, also known as the bordered white moth, was regarded as of little importance until 1953 when the first serious epidemic requiring artificial control occurred. Since then the moth has had to be controlled from the air on eight separate occasions. On larch the larch web-spinning sawfly *Cephalcia alpina* caused widespread damage of Japanese larch for the first time in 1972, having been first recorded in Britain only in 1954. Among the spruce sawflies *Gilpinia hercyniae* (Forestry Commission Record 117*), first recorded in Britain in 1906, made its debut as a serious pest of Sitka and Norway spruces in 1968 in north and central Wales. The small spruce sawfly *Pristiphora abietina*, for a longer time recognised as a pest in Britain, has also the capacity to cause quite serious defoliation and dieback of shoots, with consequent crown distortion following. Two other larch feeding species, *Anoplonyx destructor* and *Pristiphora westmaeli*, also occasionally cause heavy crown browning and needle loss. In general the control of defoliators is a complicated operation, since usually fairly large areas are affected, and special equipment has to be used. The best advice that can be given is that when trouble arises expert guidance should be sought. The Forestry Commission's Entomology Branch should always be informed of reports of outbreaks and will readily offer advice.

Bark and wood feeders

Bark and ambrosia beetles and weevils are, in the main, secondary pests whose numbers are dependent on the provision of suitable breeding sites in the form of debilitated or damaged trees or felled produce. Multiplication normally takes place beneath the bark. When numbers of these insects are high they can under certain circumstances, attack and damage healthy growing crops. The most important British problems are connected with bark beetles on spruce, pine and larch and also weevils on the pines. The insects concerned are the weevils *Pissodes* spp. (Forestry Commission Leaflet 29*), and the bark beetles *Dendroctonus micans*, the great spruce bark beetle (Forestry Commission Bulletins 38* and 85), *Tomicus piniperda*, pine shoot beetle (Forestry Commission Leaflet 3*), and *Ips cembrae*, the larch bark beetle. The last is a fairly recent introduction to this country, having first been recorded in 1956, and is so far confined in distribution to eastern Scotland and one known location in north-east England.

The young adults of *Tomicus piniperda* and *Ips cembrae* feed by boring into twigs or branches. In the case of *T. piniperda* they bore up to the centre of young, usually 1 year old, shoots and in *I. cembrae* in the cambium and wood, girdling branches up to 4 years old. These damaged parts break off and, since the leading shoot is often involved, permanent and serious distortions of the main stem can result. Control can be achieved by maintaining a good standard of forest hygiene, and it is thus a manage-

Tomicus piniperda damage to Scots pine shoot.

Dendroctonus micans, the great spruce bark beetle.

rial rather than a strictly entomological problem. As a general rule it is wise to ensure that stems which are felled in thinning and clearing operations are not left in the forest long enough for a brood to be produced from them. Material, therefore, should not be left in the forest for more than 6 weeks from the time of felling, during the period from April through to July, in the case of *T. piniperda*, and from April to September for *I. cembrae*. If removal within this time limit is not feasible the bark beetle brood should be destroyed either by debarking the timber or by spraying it with an approved insecticide. Forestry Commission Leaflet 3* gives further details of the methods which should be employed. Good forest hygiene is also effective in controlling numbers of *Pissodes* weevils.

The great spruce bark beetle *D. micans* is a serious pest throughout Europe and is now well established in Britain, having been discovered here in 1982. It breeds under the bark in extensive chambers and all stages of the beetle may be found at any time of the year. All species of spruce are susceptible and attacks can cause not only death of large patches of

Rhizophagus grandis predator of *Dendroctonus micans*.

bark resulting in severe damage and distortion to the trunk but also death of the tree. Attacks are generally signalled by abnormal resin bleeding with obvious tubes of resin exuding from the stem. These may even be produced from roots just below the litter. If it is suspected that spruce has been attacked by this bark beetle, rapid action is necessary and advice on identification and control will readily be given by the Forestry Commission's Entomology Branch. From 1984 the Entomology Branch of this Division has been rearing the predatory beetle *Rhizophagus grandis* for use in a biological control programme against *D. micans*.

Stem feeders

Insects that feed on tree stems comprise another category which may be the cause of direct or indirect losses. The more important species belong either to the family of so-called scale insects or to the woolly aphids or adelgids. The felted beech coccus *Cryptococcus fagisuga* (Forestry Commission Leaflet 15*) may produce unsightly quantities of waxy wool on the stems and branches of forest and amenity beech trees. Its association with the fungus *Nectria coccinea* is well known. A joint attack of these two organisms can cause a serious canker and dieback condition in beech crops (Forestry Commission Bulletin 69 *Beech bark disease*). The ash scale *Pseudochermes fraxini* is associated with, and may be a contributory cause of, a debilitating condition of ash. Among conifers conspicuous stem infestation may be seen on *Abies* spp., particularly on *A. grandis* by *Adelges piceae*, as well as on *Pinus strobus* by *Pineus strobi*. Infestations on *Abies* sometimes lead to a form of timber degrade or reaction wood termed 'Rotholz'. Infestation on *Pinus strobus* appears to have no noticeable direct effect although stems affected are often also attacked by the pathogenic rust fungus *Cronartium ribicola*.

Use of insecticides

The use of insecticides in forest practice is small and falls into two main categories. In nurseries, insecticides are used relatively frequently, as in horticultural practice, to ensure the production of clean, healthy planting stock of good form. In plantations, use of insecticides is almost entirely restricted to applications to prevent anticipated death of trees and therefore reduction in stocking or, in the worst cases, wholesale destruction of crops, rather than against attacks resulting only in some loss of growth in infested trees and perhaps damage to tree form. It should be borne in mind that in many instances established trees are able to tolerate, and make a good recovery from apparently quite severe defoliation; other problems, e.g. bark-beetle attack, may be more serious. The use of insecticides in plantations is restricted by environmental as well as economic considerations and the former particularly includes the fact that for large-scale operations, or in any case for the treatment of crops which have closed canopy, aerial application may be the only practical means, requiring very adequate justification.

As mentioned above in relation to the control of *Hylobius abietis* and *Hylastes* spp. the use of insecticides is governed by the Control of Pesticides Regulations 1986. Insecticides to be used in forestry (as for other purposes) must have one of two forms of Approval under these regulations. Manufacturers of pesticides apply to the Pesticide Safety Division of the Ministry of Agriculture, Fisheries and Food for 'Label' Approval for the anticipated commercial uses of their products. If all of the authorities' data requirements, mainly concerning the safety of the product, have been met satisfactorily the product will be given Full Approval. If some data requirements are outstanding the product may be given only Provisional Approval covering a limited period during which the manufacturer is expected to satisfy the further requirements. A Provisional Approval may also be Restricted with regard to the extent of use, e.g. in terms of the total area which may be treated. It quite often happens that a manufacturer has not sought approval for some particular use of a product either because he does not see it as having commercial potential and/or because the use is particularly specialised. It is then open to a user to apply for an 'Off-label' Approval for the use of the product for a particular purpose. In these circumstances the use of the product is at the user's own risk rather than that of the manufacturer. 'Off-label' Approvals may also be for a limited period of time and/or be restricted with regard to the amount of use. Applicants for 'Off-label' Approvals may be required to produce an 'Application Leaflet', which is equivalent to a manufacturer's label, describing how the product is to be used.

> The seemingly technical distinctions between 'Label' and 'Off-label' Approvals are of importance because many actual and prospective uses of insecticides in forestry are not covered by 'Label' Approvals. 'Off-label' Approvals tend to be short term and the approval process may take some time. It is therefore not appropriate to give details in this publication. The Forestry Commission's Entomology Branch should be consulted for up-to-date information on all prospective uses of insecticides relating to plantations.

For forest nursery crops before final planting out (among other categories of non-edible crops and plants) a broad group of 'Off-label' arrangements has been made for the use of any product which already has 'Label' Approval, subject to certain conditions which are described in The Pesticide Register and should be studied.

8 Wildlife management

Woodland wildlife encompasses the whole range of living organisms including all the plants and animals, together with the non-living elements that make up the woodland ecosystem. Woodland management will include, ecological, silvicultural, recreational, economic and landscape considerations. Wildlife management will encompass tree protection, conservation and exploitation objectives.

Objectives and priorities

The objectives of managing wildlife in forests fall into three groups:

- preventing damage to forest or farm crops;
- utilising forest wildlife for amenity, recreation, sport and meat;
- conserving ecosystems, communities and species.

Damage can be reduced by:

- keeping damaging wildlife away;
- reducing numbers of damaging animals.

Conservation of species and communities can be achieved best by managing habitats. The management of forests to increase the range of habitats present, by increasing structural diversity, will improve the wildlife value of forests. However, the range of habitats and ecological niches provided should reflect the physical/chemical conditions of the site, and not pursue a degree of artificiality suggestive of 'gardening', and requiring high inputs for maintenance.

The forester and wildlife manager need to be able to predict problems arising from normal forest practices. To do this they need to recognise the local wildlife of importance for damage, utilisation or conservation, predict for a five year span or thereabouts what changes there will be in the areas of woodland at risk, consider to what extent achieving damage prevention must be integrated with local farm or estate interests and priorities, and consider how changing forest succession and practices may affect species and habitats with conservation or amenity values.

Wildlife management can only succeed when objectives and priorities are clearly stated. These are not necessarily mutually compatible. For example, pheasant production may be more important than squirrel control, or access for deer utilisation. Then such sources of conflict should be anticipated and the loss in timber value from squirrel damage, loss in venison and habitat damage by deer, recognised as a cost attributable to pheasant production.

Preventing damage by wildlife

Crop protection

Wildlife management should aim to be predictive. The impact of pest species on the crop should be estimated and if the expected level of damage would reduce crop values significantly, tactics for prevention should be put into practice. Sometimes prevention is not possible, and reduction of existing damage is necessary. The amount of damage should be measured to provide information against which the cost of action can be assessed.

113

P.R. Ratcliffe, Head of Wildlife and Conservation Research Branch

Types of damage

Browsing is the removal, by biting, of apical buds of all or part of the current year's growth of foliage or shoots. On occasion part of the previous year's growth may also be removed. Browsing is usually for food and can occur at any time of year but is most common in winter and during the period of shoot elongation in spring. This is the most widespread form of damage affecting young trees before the leading shoot is out of reach. It is rarely significant on mature trees and shrubs unless the form and shape are of amenity value. Browsing may result in reduced height and diameter and in deformation such as bushing or multiple leadering, but rarely death. Different tree species have different growth responses to browsing pressure and also vary in susceptibility in different parts of the country. It is usually sufficient to measure browsing damage by assessing the proportion of trees with missing leaders to obtain an estimate of crop damage.

Stripping is the removal by biting of bark from the main stem. Different animals attack different species and age classes of tree at various times of year. Stripping may result in tree death if the tree is girdled. Wind snap may occur particularly in conifers even when less than the whole bark circumference has been removed. Timber degrade is inevitable as the tree calluses over and some species are susceptible to rotting and staining organisms entering through the exposed wound surface.

Fraying is specifically attributed to deer using their antlers to abrade and partially remove the bark from stems and branches. The bark often hangs in strips in tatters. This kills or deforms the tree but in woodland conditions only relatively few trees in small areas are affected. Conversely damage may quickly reach unacceptable proportions where specimen amenity trees are concerned. Fraying may be done at various times of the year (predictable for

Roe deer damage – stripping.

Damage to mature Sitka spruce by red deer.

Bark stripping by grey squirrel.

Roe deer damage – browsing.

different deer species) to help remove velvet from antlers, to mark territory or as part of aggressive behaviour during the mating season.

Girdling (ring barking) is bark removal at any height on the stem from fraying or stripping around the complete circumference of main stem or branch and results in the death of the tree or branch beyond that point.

Bud removal is eating of apical or lateral buds. This is rarely sufficiently widespread to reduce increment except when associated with shoot or foliage removal.

Uprooting. Red deer especially, can be responsible for pulling out newly planted trees over large areas.

Grey squirrel approaching baited hopper.

Table 8.1 Mammal species damaging forest trees

Animal	Time and type of damage				National distribution of animal	Protection measures*
	Browsing	*Stripping*	*Fraying*	*Other*		
Roe deer *Capreolus capreolus*	Autumn to spring		March to July		Southern England; northern Britain; invading mid-wales.	Fencing, tree guards/shelters, shooting. Close seasons for all except muntjac. Deer doing damage during the close season may only be shot in specific circumstance.
Red deer *Cervus elaphus*	Autumn to spring	Any time	March to May		Scotland; some English populations.	
Sika deer *Cervus nippon*	Autumn to spring	Any time	March to May	Bole scoring	Spreading in west and north Scotland; some English populations.	
Fallow deer *Dama dama*	Autumn to spring	Occasional	March to May	Feeding on farm crops	Midlands and southern England; few Welsh and Scottish populations.	
Muntjac deer *Munticus reevesi*	Autumn to spring	Occasional	March to May		Spreading through southern Britain.	
Feral goats *Capra* (domestic)	Autumn to spring	Occasional			Scattered populations in uplands of England. Scotland and Wales.	Populations may be of conservation importance.
Sheep *Ovis* (domestic)	At any time				Main alternative land use in upland Britain.	Must be kept out by fencing. Should be herded out not shot, when woodlands are invaded.
Rabbit *Oryctolagus cuniculus*	Autumn to spring occasionally summer	Winter, particularly during prolonged snow cover		Grazing farm crops	Widespread.	November to March – poisoning (phosphine or cyanide). Fencing, tree guards/shelters. Legal obligation to control rabbits.
Brown hare *Lepus capensis*	Winter and spring clipping shoots				Locally abundant. Widespread in lowlands.	Shooting.

Animal	Time and type of damage				National distribution of animal	Protection measures*
	Browsing	*Stripping*	*Fraying*	*Other*		
Blue hare *Lepus timidus*	Winter and spring clipping shoots				Widespread in uplands.	Shooting.
Field vole *Microtus agrestis*		Any time, particularly late winter to spring			Widespread.	Tree guards. Use monitoring methods to predict potentially damaging peaks in numbers.
Bank vole *Clethrionomys glareolus*		Occasional		Widespread		
Grey squirrel *Sciurus carolinensis*		May–July		Seed cones; walnut and chestnut Horticultural crops	Southern Britain and lowland Scotland.	Poisoning April–July (0.02% warfarin on whole wheat). Illegal in specified counties with red squirrels.

*The law relating to the conservation and control of wildlife is complex. *An introduction to animal law* by Margaret E. Cooper (Academic Press) provides a valuable summary and discussion.

Damaging animal species

The animals most likely to cause damage in British forests are listed in Table 8.1. The relative importance of expected damage types has been indicated but the extent to which they have an important impact varies with local site factors. These include tree species and provenances, area and shape of coupe and presence of alternative food plants. The latter may be modified by forest practices such as weeding and fertilising the tree crop. It is particularly important to consider whether changing forest practices or successional changes are likely to affect the local animals over the period that a crop is at risk.

Damage assessment and methods of prevention

Once the degree of risk has been estimated then the least costly action can be taken. Where risk is low regular inspection backed by 'fire brigade' action if necessary is appropriate. Inspection is particularly important in low risk situations, such as where there are climatic problems, (e.g. heavy snow allowing break-ins by sheep or deer) or with animals such as field voles whose numbers fluctuate over a 3–5 year cycle.

In high risk situations it is important to consider the relative costs and efficiencies of animal control measures (which usually have a high labour content) and of tree protection techniques (with a high capital content). Habitat modifications rarely prevent damage altogether although they may reduce it significantly and may improve the efficiency of the other techniques. When inspections reveal apparently significant damage levels, a damage assessment (Forestry Commission Leaflet 82 *Assessment of wildlife damage in forests*) should be done.

Protection techniques

These include fencing, individual tree protection and chemical repellants. Individual tree protection is often cheaper than fencing on small areas of less than 2–3 hectares. Chemical repellants are neither as cheap nor as effective as individual tree guards for large-scale forest use and are seldom justified.

The use of fencing to prevent forest damage should not be confused with its more common agricultural roles of enclosing stock and marking boundaries. In general fencing is at its cheapest in cost per hectare protected when used for areas over 25–40 hectares.

Control techniques

These include shooting, trapping and poisoning. All of them are constrained by legislation for use on particular species in particular circumstances and at certain times of year. The Wildlife and Countryside Act 1981 and recent revisions to schedules provide the most comprehensive guides and refer to other relevant Acts. Table 8.1 indicates the methods appropriate for the main damaging forest animals.

As far as possible the aim is to kill the individual animals responsible for or expected to do the damage while not placing other species at risk. Killing without reference to damage prevented is irresponsible and a waste of resources. Practical experience and effective training, in learning how and when to use such techniques, are vital for foresters and wildlife managers. A knowledge of the biology of the species, and of the available techniques for measuring important demographic parameters, such as reproduction, mortality and density, is essential for prediction.

Habitat modification

The most important habitat modifications are concerned with making damaging animals more accessible for control. Such techniques include the provision of glades where deer can be safely shot. While a certain amount of success has been gained, for example, from provision of willows to reduce fraying in upland sites, there is no good evidence on the value of planting alternative browse without also increasing control of deer. There is little evidence that increasing the number of predators by, for example, putting in nest boxes and retaining raptor nest sites may reduce the likelihood of field vole populations reaching damaging peaks. Habitat modification is of much greater importance when there is a conservation objective, especially when such action ensures increased diversity.

Other considerations

The requirements of woodland wildlife management cannot be considered in isolation from neighbouring land use. It may be necessary to agree mutual policies over animals such as deer and rabbits. Where the same animals may be damaging in one land use system and of value to the neighbour then exclusion and tactics following break-ins must be agreed, e.g.

for sheep and red deer. Traditional country sporting activities may well be pursued if they do not interfere with normal forest practice. It should be noted, however, that there is little evidence that deer hunting is more efficient in preventing damage by specific animals than is control by shooting. There may be legal requirements such as for rabbit management in neighbours interests. The use of snares for killing foxes is inhumane and unselective and should be discouraged.

Conservation

The first objective for conservation in forestry practice is to define and manage sites of special interest where conservation objectives will take priority over all other land use objectives. These sites should be identified on a conservation plan, the second objective is to increase the variety of wildlife present within the physical and chemical limitation of the site.

In order to achieve these objectives the presence of conservation features must be identified and their location adequately mapped. The significance and therefore the priority to be attached to their management must be understood and the extent of legal obligations and constraints on forest practices must be recognised and incorporated into conservation plans.

The Forestry Commission's *Forest nature conservation guidelines* gives essential information and guidance for forest managers. The reader of this chapter is directed to that publication for further guidance and advice.

Protection of sites and species

Geological features and ancient monuments of national significance are usually notified by the

THE CONSERVATION PLAN

It is particularly important to check the status of land prior to afforestation or of woodland prior to reafforestation. Over the last two decades or so the proportions of unafforested moorland in the uplands and of ancient broadleaved woodland in the lowlands have decreased. This means that further inroads into either may have greater consequences in relation to the total available now than was the case in the past. Information is available from regional officers of English Nature, Scottish Natural Heritage and the Countryside Council for Wales, or from bodies such as the local Naturalist Trust or the Royal Society for the Protection of Birds. The Wildlife and Countryside Act 1981 and its 1985 amendment also controls the disturbance, removal or killing of a variety of plants, birds and other animals. It is the duty of the forest manager to be aware of the presence of such wildlife and to ensure that forest operations are not destructive. There is therefore a need for the existence and location of conservation features to be accurately identified and the legal and practical constraints to be recognised as part of the operational forest planning. The most useful method found so far is the preparation of the conservation plan which records on maps the site or sub-compartment in which such limits operate. It is for the forest manager to ensure that contractors are aware of damage they may inadvertently do. The reasons for conservation interest and limits on operations can be detailed in the conservation plan, parts of which may need to be confidential if the safety of particular habitats or species is to be assured.

appropriate authorities. They are more likely to be at risk during the processes of afforestation than in the course of subsequent forest operations. As they are fixed points their accurate location on maps and on the ground is relatively straightforward and there is no reason why subsequent forest operations should affect them.

The plants and animals which are of importance in wildlife conservation may be more difficult to manage. However, under the Wildlife and Countryside Act 1981, English Nature, Scottish Natural Heritage and the Countryside Council for Wales have a duty to notify landowners of the boundaries of sites of special scientific interest (SSSIs) and of the operations which may affect the site and for which prior notification of forest operations is required. Since a number of normal lawful operations (fertilising, herbicide use, draining, etc.) may have indirect adverse consequences it is essential that these are discussed. These discussions should take place well in advance since the programme for forest operations is usually planned months or even years in advance.

Background to positive conservation

While the objectives described above are essentially concerned with the protection of existing assets, increasing the variety of wildlife offers great scope for positive action by foresters. The distribution and abundance of wildlife in Britain is rarely entirely natural, it has mostly been established and maintained by previous forms of woodland or land management. In the lowlands the association of woodland wildlife with coppice is the prime example and in the uplands moorland fauna and flora were established by deforestation and maintained by traditional forms of management. Accordingly where established forms of land use are to be changed, active conservation management is required to maintain traditional wildlife features. Wildlife associated with

new forms of land management should not necessarily, however, be regarded as inferior. The development of a flora or fauna in new forest plantations can constitute an enrichment for the area as a whole. Encouragement of new communities in a changed landscape can therefore be as important as maintaining continuity elsewhere. As these communities develop they will, through time, increase in conservation value.

Forest and woodland wildlife can be manipulated by adopting particular forms of forestry practice, some of which will be more expensive than others. Ideally an owner should calculate the cost to his forest management and decide what he is prepared to pay. Consequently foresters must be aware of the means of developing or maintaining wildlife to best advantage. Many measures designed to benefit wildlife will also benefit sporting, recreation and the landscape. This should be taken into account when plans are being formulated and costed.

CONTINUITY AND DIVERSITY

The two most important concepts in wildlife conservation are continuity and diversity. Continuity is more important in long established woodland, especially ancient woodland, where wildlife features of value already exist and need to be conserved and where sudden and extreme change can drastically alter ecosystems which have taken centuries to develop. Diversity is more important in new afforestation schemes which by definition do not have an established woodland fauna and flora. Here the need is to create diversity of habitats to produce diversity of wildlife.

It should be recognised at the outset that wildlife management for conservation is rarely a clearly defined matter. What is best for one animal or plant may not be appropriate for another and may conflict with timber growing. Similarly the relationship between management input and conservation benefit has not been precisely quantified. Therefore forest managers cannot easily know if a particular level of economic loss will produce a worthwhile conservation benefit.

Lowland woods and forests
Value of existing woodlands

Most lowland woods are on old broadleaved woodland sites which are often now of only limited extent. They are usually fertile and are therefore capable of supporting vigorous growth of many plant species. Where the woodland site is ancient, that is it has been wooded since medieval times, the flora is particularly rich in plants which may have difficulty colonising new plantations. This applies both to ancient high forest sites and to coppice, although the quantity of ground vegetation is often much greater under the latter. Woodlands on agricultural and heathland are remarkably less rich, particularly in rare herbs, although those on calcareous soils may be an exception. The total number of wildlife species generally increases with the size of forest blocks.

Choice of crop system and species

Long rotations, small-scale group felling, coppicing, overwood or other two-storey systems and an even distribution of age classes will all contribute to continuity and diversity. Where natural regeneration is inadequate but there is ample woody weed growth to afford the necessary side shelter, planting broadleaves at wide spacing is to be preferred, so that ground and shrub layers can develop freely. Treeshelters providing protection and faster early growth at modest cost combine well with such a technique.

When weeding, a useful compromise is spot or strip chemical weeding except for rhododendron which should wherever possible be eradicated. Non-essential cleaning to remove broadleaved species should be avoided and the operation generally confined to releasing potential crop trees.

Native species of trees and shrubs are generally superior for wildlife conservation because native plants and animals have evolved with them. For instance, the timing of their leaf break and leaf fall closely matches the flowering behaviour of native woodland plants. Native trees and shrubs often support a wealth of insects which in turn supports a diverse bird population and together with the associated ground flora they are the food plants of a number of butterflies.

Although species native to the locality are to be preferred, the recently introduced southern beech has been found to support a wide variety of insects and ground plants, as do some long naturalised exotics such as larch and sycamore.

Edges

Edges are especially valuable for enriching and retaining wildlife. Wide rides of the order of 10 metres or more are particularly important in the lowlands, where with sensitive management a rich flora and fauna can often be sustained. Ride widening should be considered when marking for thinning. To develop a vegetation and habitat gradient towards the wood the edges should be cut less frequently and later in the year (mid September/October) leaving established shrubs. This favours biennial and perennial plants and the effect may be further improved by cutting opposite sides alternately. Central strips should be mown and the cut material removed, to favour summer flowering low herbs. Such rides should be permanent to allow establishment of slow colonising species and to provide continuity. Similar beneficial treatments can be applied to forest road edges.

Drainage ditches at the sides of rides and roads provide further habitat diversity. Gaps sufficient for sunshine to reach the woodland floor provide habitats not only for woodland plants and birds but also reptiles and amphibians (Forestry Commission Research Information Note 126 *Enhancement of lowland forest ridesides and roadsides to benefit wild plants and butterflies*).

Thinning

Where old woodland sites have been restocked with conifers, early and heavy thinning will help to minimise losses of plant species during the period of maximum canopy shading. In new plantations heavy thinning on a short cycle will maintain plants and help to build up a reserve of seed, rhizomes and bulbs in the soil.

Final felling

Mature, overmature and dead trees support rich epiphyte and invertebrate populations and provide numerous birds with essential foraging and breeding sites. They are also necessary for cavity dwelling bats. Retention of some overmature trees is desirable and wherever possible unmerchantable branchwood of broadleaves should be left on the ground to rot. Burning should be avoided because although it enriches the soil locally the improvement is only temporary and it causes long-established ground plants to be replaced by ephemeral and invasive species such as fireweed and nettle. Clear fellings should be dispersed if possible to avoid creating large, more or less even-aged, stands.

Semi-natural lime wood in north Lincolnshire.

Restocking

The choice of species is constrained by the requirements of the broadleaves policy but will generally favour conservation. This phase provides considerable opportunity for positive conservation initiatives.

Ride widening for improved vegetation management.

Upland forests

Afforestation

Much upland afforestation represents a sudden and fundamental change of vegetation from moorland and bog to woodland. There is a risk of losing or radically altering some plant and animal communities of local or national importance. Because of this, consultation procedures must be observed and consideration must be given to important or sensitive ecosystems, habitats and species.

Potential of plantation forests

Most upland forests were established on land of low fertility which was previously maintained as open moorland for sheep, grouse or red deer. Although the potential of the new forest for habitat diversity will largely depend upon the nature of the original site, diversity can be increased by planting a range of species, by arranging felling and restocking to produce structural variety (see Chapter 17 'Planning for the second rotation') and by leaving areas unplanted to provide non-forest habitats. The native Caledonian pinewoods of Scotland are a special case, limited in extent but of high conservation value because of their ancient origin and associated specialised fauna and flora. Similarly, valley oak and birchwoods may have an existing woodland wildlife which requires that they be considered in the same way as lowland woods.

Choice of crop system and species

Sitka spruce provides a habitat for a variety of songbirds but the usual dense canopy provides little opportunity for the establishment of a ground flora other than ferns, bryophytes and fungi, and occasionally a few vascular plants such as bilberry and heath bedstraw, unless it has been heavily thinned or allowed to grow beyond normal rotation age.

Therefore larch and pine with their light canopies and heavier ground cover provide better opportunities. Also it is well established that grand fir and Douglas fir can support rich and varied flora on well drained fertile soils. In mature stands the ground flora under these trees and indeed under heavily thinned spruce may contain a similar species list to that of neighbouring oak and so offer some prospect for limited expansion of a woodland flora in upland forests. They are also likely to support more small mammals together with their predators.

Native broadleaves are the first choice to provide habitat diversity. Where resources are limited modest block plantings on more sheltered sites are likely to give greater overall wildlife benefit than a low percentage admixture to a large area of conifers. Oak, birch, willow, rowan and alder are valuable for birds either for their seeds or their associated insects. Existing broadleaves will rarely be of any commercial value in the uplands but as their extent will usually be very limited, and their conservation benefits greater, they should be retained. They may be reinforced by planting the same species while retaining some of the existing woodland glades.

Structural diversity may be achieved vertically where conifers, especially light demanders, on sheltered fertile sites can be heavily thinned from an early age and grown beyond economic maturity on sites that are not susceptible to windthrow. Spatial diversity can be provided by ensuring that there is a good juxtaposition of different age classes including establishment, prethicket, thicket and if possible, thinned crops.

All age classes provide good habitats for songbirds. Middle aged stands are favoured by the sparrowhawk and older stands by such species as goshawk and tawny owl. The use of nest boxes can encourage birds and bats which would not otherwise find suitable nesting sites in conifer stands.

Raptors such as the barn owl and tawny owl need nest sites in good feeding areas. Nest boxes can help in young plantations.

Edges and gaps

Leaving certain areas unplanted to provide non-forest habitats can be done in many ways. Areas which are clearly unplantable due to exposure, rock, water, etc., will automatically be left, but trees should not be planted close to such features. In marginal cases or where future extraction will be difficult the question of whether forestry investment is worthwhile should be carefully considered.

Areas above the upper planting limit may be too exposed for vigorous growth of heather but on extensive areas of intermediate zones, controlled rotational burning can maintain habitat variety for moorland birds. Alternatively, a succession to natural birch woodland would have conservation benefits. Rare mosses and liverworts will survive in areas of scree and in rock gullies, but some of the rarer dwarf plants of the uplands will only survive if their more vigorous competitors are grazed.

Roads and rides have a large edge to area ratio which can be maximised by ensuring that roads and rides are wide enough from the outset so that the deep crowns which develop on the plantation edges do not have to be cut back later on. The edge effect is improved by maintaining a shrubby edge, including natural regeneration of broadleaves or conifers. When natural regeneration does not occur the planting of scattered broadleaved trees and shrubs should be considered. Roads and rides can provide a permanent network of field and dwarf shrub layer habitat, enriched along roadsides by the associated soil disturbance and sometimes by the addition of imported limestone road material and by roadside drains. Widths should be sufficient (preferably at least 10 metres) to avoid substantial shading as the crop develops.

Open areas (deer glades) are necessary for culling deer and as they will often be located at the more fertile sites in order to attract deer they are also likely to have a valuable flora and associated insect fauna. Browsing by deer can help to conserve the low growing plant species which depend upon the grazing regime for survival, and therefore fertile areas left specifically as deer glades and areas left open primarily for conservation of flora can both perform a dual role. However, it is unlikely that deer grazing alone will maintain swards of high diversity and some management such as vegetation cutting using a swipe may be required. Such conservation areas should not be fertilised or reseeded although some deer glades may need such treatment. Sites identified as having uncommon plant or animal species or communities should remain unplanted and adjacent planting kept well back from them. No fertilising or reseeding should be carried out.

Unregulated grazing by farm stock or access for shelter can be damaging particularly to rides and old broadleaf woodland sites. Downfalls for red deer in the Highlands to reach their wintering grounds should be provided at the afforestation stage.

WATER

Probably the most important category of gap is that provided by stream and lake margins. By combining water, shelter and usually better soils in a network throughout the forest, these margins have a high wildlife potential. In order to achieve this, conifers should not be planted close to the water's edge (see the Forestry Commission's publication *Forests and water guidelines*) and some broadleaved trees and shrubs should be introduced where they do not already exist. These measures also help to provide the best environment for fish and other freshwater life. In addition the rate of surface water runoff into streams and the amount of silt deposition should be reduced by leaving a buffer zone between ploughing and the watercourse and by carefully aligning main drains for gentle gradients.

Thinning and felling

The more frequent the thinning operations the shorter will be the dark periods through which plants must survive as dormant seed, rhizomes, etc. Although only a limited ground flora becomes normally established under upland Sitka spruce, the seeds of many common plants will survive the rotation and therefore even when Sitka spruce is the main species short rotation forestry is likely to have an interesting ground cover in the establishment and pre-thicket stages at each restocking. This is significant because with shorter rotations these stages represent a greater proportion of the rotation length and therefore the forest area. The ground vegetation will support a range of herbivorous animals which will, in turn support predators.

The pattern of felling also has an important influence. Although smaller felling coupes have a greater edge to area ratio which in some circumstances will support a greater density of birds, reasonably large coupes may better accommodate birds with larger territories such as short-eared owl and kestrel and therefore support a greater variety of bird species. Isolated mature trees provide valuable raptor perches and the retention of some wind snapped or dead trees of more than 30 cm diameter will encourage cavity nesting birds.

Good watercourse management in a young plantation.

Conduct of harvesting operations

During timber extraction and stacking in both uplands and lowlands efforts should be made to avoid damage to watercourses and small sensitive sites such as badger setts. Timing of these operations should also seek to avoid the flowering period where there is a rich spring flora, and felling should avoid clumps of trees in which raptor nests occur. Felling debris, harvesting machines and all chemicals should be kept out of streams and fire ponds should be constructed alongside, not by damming them. In the uplands in particular, large-scale burning of lop and top after clear felling may encourage soil erosion and adversely affect water quality.

Amenity and sport

Wildlife may be utilised for amenity or for sport. Wildlife management for amenity usually requires habitat manipulation. Planting shrubs and non-timber trees around car parks, camp sites and picnic places or for landscape reasons has a value for increasing wildlife diversity, when the scale is large enough, and thus provides a spin-off for conservation. However, it is important not to confuse amenity, landscaping and recreation with conservation, as the means for achieving these objectives may not always be compatible.

A range of wildlife species can be attracted to particular areas for viewing by the public. The establishment of sanctuary areas, where deer are not molested, can be useful. Deer soon become accustomed to these areas and can readily be approached by people. Normal deer control can be pursued in other parts of the forest. Such an example of zoning is a very useful approach to multi-objective woodland management.

A range of woodland animals can be utilised for sport. They include pheasant, woodcock, wood-pigeon, rabbit, grey squirrel, hare and deer. Wetlands, lakes and rivers may attract a range of wildfowl as well as providing fishing. Wildlife management for game and fish production involves the same range of methods as damage prevention. The main conflict with a damage prevention objective is usually over the levels of population. For example, sporting interests may encourage densities of deer which are higher than desirable for damage prevention if the species concerned is to be easily harvested. Additional problems arise where, for example, predatory animals such as stoats are destroyed in the interests of maintaining harvestable game bird surpluses. Predator control should be very carefully considered before any commitment is made, and generally discouraged in the interest of conservation.

> It is always important to define the objectives in woodland management and to allocate priorities if conflicts are envisaged.

9   Fire protection

The size, location and nature of a woodland estate dictate the level of fire precautions and fire fighting capacity which can be justified. The various options available are described in this chapter but it is the owner's responsibility to assess his own situation and to select the most appropriate scheme. It is possible to insure against fire losses but insurance companies usually require reasonable precautions to reduce fire danger.

Fire danger is a combination of *fire risk* and *fire hazard*. Fire risk is defined as the likelihood of a fire starting. It increases with the presence of people especially children, day trippers and other holidaymakers and with the presence of neighbouring moorland during the heather and grass burning seasons in the uplands or harvested cornfield if stubble burning is practised. Fire hazard is the susceptibility of vegetation to burn if a fire occurs. It depends on the kind of vegetation present, its flammability and the wind force and relative humidity. There may be no fire danger even in very dry conditions if there is no risk of a fire being started nor for example if large numbers of people are about but the vegetation is wet. There is extreme fire danger, however, if high risk of a fire being started occurs when an area is in a highly hazardous condition.

Fire protection methods

Fire protection methods try to prevent fires by reducing the risk and to limit the size of a fire when one starts.

An owner should personally maintain good rela-

CONSULTATION WITH FIRE SERVICE

The Local Authority Fire Services have the statutory responsibility for dealing with all uncontrolled fires and therefore an important part of planning should be consultation with the local Fire Service. They are willing, within the level of staff availability, to help owners by discussing the best means of preventing and tackling fires on their properties. Annual contact is recommended.

tions with his neighbours. People generally take more care when they appreciate the danger and good neighbours can be an important source of help in reporting fires or even helping to fight them.

Woodmen and contractors

It should be impressed on everyone who works in the woods that they are responsible for taking the utmost care with all types of fires. Estate and woodland staff should be reminded of fire danger especially when fire hazard increases after a spell of little or no danger. Contracts for the sale of timber or for carrying out forest operations should always include clauses defining responsibility for fire precautions and for compensation for any damage incurred. In practice it is useless to try to prohibit all smoking by workmen in the woods. A more practical line is to lay down times and places where workmen may

129

J.B. Teasdale, former Safety Officer

smoke, explaining the precautions to be observed and insist upon compliance.

Reducing the risk of a fire spreading from nearby ground

Fire breaks

These are semi-permanent strips kept clear of inflammable vegetation and having a width of at least 10 m. If possible their surface should be firm and level enough to allow access and movement of vehicles and equipment for fire fighting. A fire spreading from adjoining land has time to build up in size and fire fighting teams may have to be deployed along a considerable length of boundary in order to stop it. Fire breaks are an expensive form of protection and therefore an attempt should be made to assess the likelihood of fire and the value of the crop at risk reconciling these with the cost of preparing the break. There are various means of preparing and maintaining breaks and these are described and compared in Table 9.1.

Normally the plantation or land ownership boundary dictates the position of fire breaks but topographical features can be used to reinforce their effectiveness. Ridges, brows of hills and physical barriers like streams have obvious advantages. On occasion a break can be set up some way inside a plantation if the cost of protection benefits gained will justify the higher risk of losing the plantation left between the break and the boundary. The effect of the proposed barrier on the landscape must also be borne in mind.

Methods aimed at prevention

Publicity

Statistics indicate that the public by accident or intent, are responsible for about 80% of fires on or immediately adjacent to Forestry Commission land.

Almost all other fires spread from adjoining land, often the result of careless burning by farmers or from railways and the like. The Commission makes use of opportunities offered by the press, radio and television both nationally and locally to make the public more aware of forest fire danger, concentrating its effort in the periods of highest danger. Details of fire losses and the damage done to fauna and flora by fire are publicised in order to increase public awareness. Staff involved with the public take the opportunity to stress the risk of fire when talking to schools or colleges or simply meeting people at a picnic site or walking in the forest.

If a private owner considers that the conditions called for publicity in the news media, he should, in order to ensure proper co-ordination, make representations to the local Forestry Commission Conservator. A more direct approach to the visiting public by such means as fire warning signs and beater stands should also be considered. Suitable signs are not cheap and therefore should be used where their message will achieve maximum effect such as areas where the public are invited or have a right to enter. Greater impact will be achieved by putting up warning signs only during fire danger periods and removing them when the danger ends. Most fire signs simply warn but some tell the public what action to take in case of fire, locating the nearest telephone and giving the appropriate number to ring. Well maintained beater racks or stands may also be used as a visual reminder of fire danger to the public as well as being immediately available in the event of fire.

Fire belts and barriers

Belts of trees which do not themselves readily catch fire can sometimes provide a useful barrier. Providing site conditions are adequate larch is a good choice. Broadleaf species usually grow too slowly

Table 9.1 Fire breaks – comparison of alternative methods

Method	Appropriate situation	Advantages	Disadvantages
Cultivation: by plough, hand tool, bulldozer or discs, usually smoothed later by tine harrow or discs.	Particularly dangerous situations, and infertile ground unsuitable for improved grazing.	No risk. Can be done in any season, subject to ground conditions. Cheap by machine.	Unless cambered and on suitable soil type may hinder access. Expensive by hand. Maintenance may be difficult on wet sites. Unsightly.
Chemicals (paraquat and glyphosate): by knapsack or machine-mounted sprayer.	Coarse grass, especially *Molinia*.	May give protection for two seasons. With hand application can be used on steep rocky ground. Suitable for wet sites.	Expensive. Not effective on calcareous soils or on some types of vegetation. Unsightly.
*Burning	Plantation boundaries where cultivation is difficult.	Suitable for a wide range of ground conditions. Will last several years on heather.	High risk. Dependent on season. Needs annual repetition on *Molinia*.
Mowing: by large gang mower or swipe.	Sites suitable for machine operation.	Good appearance. Low maintenance cost.	Mowing debris left *in situ* may become a hazard. Desiccation may reduce effectiveness during extreme drought.
Grazing: usually necessary to cultivate, fertilise and reseed.	On soils which will carry pasture grasses.	Good appearance. May be integrated with estate management.	Stock management problems, e.g. fencing. Initial cost can be high. Desiccation may reduce effectiveness during extreme drought.

*Burning
The following publications will be useful:
England and Wales

The heather and grass burning code: advice on the burning of heather and grass.
Heather and grass burning: summary of good burning practice.
Both are obtainable from any Regional or Divisional Office of MAFF or the Welsh Office Agriculture Department.
Scotland

A guide to good muirburn practice: produced jointly by DAFS and NCC and available from HMSO.
Muirburn – a code of practice. Publication No. 25; available from the Scottish Agricultural Colleges.

but where they already exist they may be retained in a continuous strip and enriched if necessary by further planting. Closer planting and complete beating up are usually required to ensure the early suppression of ground vegetation that is necessary for an effective barrier. The width of the belts is a matter of judgement, 20 metres normally being adequate. Care should be taken to integrate these belts with the landscape and it may be possible to vary the width so that the broadleaved or larch bands run up into any natural gullies, or to use some other means to break up an unnatural banded appearance while maintaining a continuous barrier. Other forms of barrier worth preserving on fire protection grounds alone include hedges, walls, ditches and watercourses. These and indeed all fire breaks should never be regarded as fireproof but only as obstacles to the rapid spread of a fire.

Brashing

Where neighbouring ground vegetation grows up to the forest edge the complete brashing of all the trees to a height of 2 metres in a 10–20 metre wide strip may stop a fire getting into the tree canopy. As the aim is to create a gap between the ground vegetation and tree branches, cut material must be removed, usually drawn back into the forest.

Methods aimed at reducing loss when a fire occurs

Breaking up a plantation into smaller blocks

Roads

As well as allowing access by vehicles with pumps and water or foam, roads are valuable as internal fire breaks and fires can be fought from them.

Rides

Ordinary untreated grass rides are not a fire barrier in themselves but once crops reach the thicket stage rides can provide access and breaks at which to fight a fire.

Changes in crop

It is a common experience when fighting a forest fire to find that its progress is checked when the fire reaches a crop of another species or age. Where the layout and scheme of management of the woods permits, it is therefore a good plan to break up large blocks by changes in species or age class.

Provision of early warning of a fire

Fire look-outs and patrols

Employing men specifically to watch for fire outbreaks is so expensive that it can be considered only at times of the most extreme fire danger. The men must be equipped with some ready means of reporting an outbreak. Fixed structure such as towers allow the installation of telephone but they are usually only appropriate for very large properties. Mobile patrols are more versatile and as well as reporting fires can warn people and tackle outbreaks. They must however be equipped with either a portable communication device such as a car phone, two way radio or a vehicle so that they can reach a telephone quickly.

Neighbours

Often neighbours are in a good position to see and warn of any fires and they can be helpful if the position of a smoke report needs verification or its cause confirmed. A list of neighbours' telephone numbers should be maintained.

133

Public

Notices should encourage members of the public to report outbreaks of fire and even to help fight them initially. It is helpful if notices give the location name.

Access and water supplies

The desirability of seeking the advice of the local Fire Service on all aspects of provision of access and water supplies cannot be overstressed.

Good access is an important factor in containing any fire. It can however be prohibitively expensive to invest capital in roads years before they are justified for timber extraction. Access provision must therefore be carefully assessed and it may be possible to carry out relatively inexpensive work to improve access while not providing roads to the loadbearing standards necessary for timber extraction. Fire Services, however, depend on good access to carry their fire fighting tenders to a fire and it is important not only to consult them about the suitability of roads but to ensure that they are acquainted with entrances from public roads which may not always be obvious. Use of the correct access route by the Fire Service and other assistance can be ensured by using *route markers*. The official recognised marker is a 3-metre length of coloured polythene streamer, red to the fire and green for the way out. Full details of use and source of supply may be obtained from the Fire Service or from the Forestry Commission.

Where roads suitable for fire service tenders cannot be provided plans should be made for Land Rovers and tractors to move Fire Service hoses and transportable pumps, estate water bowsers, other equipment and personnel to the fire. Where the use of helicopters is anticipated landing sites need to be provided if the roads themselves are inadequate for the purpose.

Water is invaluable in fire fighting and in damping down after a fire. The minimum useful static supply is considered to be 2000 litres (440 gallons) and the smallest reliable flowing supply about 5000 litres (1100 gallons) per hour with 0.6 metre depth at the pumping point. Wherever possible the damming of streams is preferred to the erection of water tanks which are often unsightly and difficult to maintain. The size and number of dams will depend on the extent of the woodland and the availability of other water supplies but bearing in mind that the standard fire service tender carries about 1800 litres (400 gallons). A reasonable size is about 20 000 litres (4400 gallons). The local Water Authority or regional water board should be consulted before impounding water as a licence may be necessary, and it should be remembered that reservoirs are attractive and therefore possibly dangerous to children and other visitors.

Fire spreading from *Molinia* moorland into Sitka spruce crop 4 m high.

All principal water supplies should be provided with vehicular access for water collection and where there is the possibility of helicopters being used to collect water in under-slung buckets, there should be a minimum water depth of 2 metres at the collecting point. Trees must be kept well back to provide the necessary flight path clearance. Where they exist water authority hydrants should be identified for use in fire fighting.

Foam

Instead of plain water, foam is now used increasingly in forest fire fighting by the Forestry Commission and some Fire Services. When used properly it enables fires to be controlled more easily with smaller manpower and pump resources. As it facilitates water economy by reducing evaporation and runoff, it enables water to be used more effectively. The visibility of foam enables the operator to see where it

has been applied. In addition to the ordinary pump, hose and water supply, a suitable foam concentrate is required together with a special branch pipe (nozzle) for foam production. A 5 hp pump and a medium expansion branch pipe are suitable for application of foam to the ground and to tree canopies up to 3 metres high, whereas a 12 hp pump and low expansion branch pipe will project it to heights of 20 metres.

Foam solution may be formed by premixing but to produce foam from a natural or a continuous artificial water supply an inductor is required to introduce the concentrate at the pump or into the hose line. Foam concentrate is non-toxic but neither the concentrate nor the solution should be flushed directly into watercourses. The same foam concentrate in very much weaker solution will produce 'wet' water which is of particular value in damping down or dealing with ground fires because of its increased power of penetration.

Beaters and other fire fighting equipment

A small readily available supply of fire fighting equipment is essential so that a fire can be tackled quickly before it grows too large to be easily extinguished. What equipment is needed depends on the scale and nature of the woodlands. For the commonest type of fire involving ground vegetation and small trees beaters are used, but some means of applying water is always useful.

Fire beaters

A number of different types are used. Birch brooms made by wiring together freshly cut birch twigs in lengths of 0.6 to 0.9 metres (2 to 3 feet) on to a springy birch pole some 1.8 metres (6 feet) long are the most common. They are of greater value in rough heather or tussock grass. Their drawback is that if

Fire in Sitka spruce plantation coming up against a foam barrier.

Beater and spray used together to extinguish a spot fire.

Alternatively, a doubled or tripled piece of rabbit netting can be attached to the pole, usually by threading spring steel wire through the outer edge of the netting and binding the ends to the pole. Both belting and netting types are best used on grass fires or where there are not too many tuffets or rocks as they cannot be used to poke out embers in awkward places.

Long-handled shovels are another option and can be used for digging embers and scattering soil as well as for beating. Hessian sacks, especially if they can be wetted, are very useful for smothering grass fires and have the advantage that a small supply can be carried in a car boot.

Other equipment

Even on a small estate some items of equipment in addition to beaters are considered essential. Wire cutters are often required for speeding up access and there should be effective torches for night work. Knapsack sprayers are needed, not only for backing up beaters but for damping down after a fire. A supply of wetting agent (ordinary household detergent or foam concentrate) is a useful addition to the knapsack pump, in order to provide better water penetration. Small canvas or plastic buckets are often invaluable for filling knapsack sprayers from forest drains and shallow streams.

In a larger estate or where the number of helpers would permit the cutting of fire lines, chain saws, axes and brush cutters should be available. Small portable pumps (about 5 hp) are useful if there is sufficient vehicular access to allow the pump to be brought within carrying distance of a fire and if there are adequate water supplies to serve the pump's rate of delivery (up to 50 gallons per minute). Portable canvas or plastic dams holding not less than 450 litres (100 gallons) are also useful. They are filled on site either by portable pumps or by the Fire Service

left in the open they remain serviceable for only one year. It is therefore best to leave a few out in the forest for propaganda and immediate fire fighting purposes and to maintain a larger stock in a covered store where they will remain serviceable for two or more years and are less likely to be removed by visitors.

Conveyor belting in pieces about 0.4 by 0.5 metres (15 × 18 inches) can be attached by small bolts to poles. To match the life of the belting the poles should be of long lasting or preservative treated wood. These beaters will last for a number of years especially if stored under cover. Any stored in the open should have the belting pads supported horizontally or hung vertically to avoid deterioration.

tender and are used in turn to supply knapsack sprayers or portable pumps. Heather burning torches are recommended where counter firing may be necessary.

Whatever equipment is chosen it should be kept close to the vehicle garage and it should not be used for any other purpose. It should always be checked prior to the start of a fire season and if possible it should not be locked away.

Training fire fighters in advance

A trained gang is far more effective than men called in only when there is an emergency. The possible saving in fire loss makes training well worthwhile and this can often be tied in with controlled burning of dangerous boundaries or the testing of fire equipment. Training should be made as realistic as possible and should include reporting the fire and transporting the men and equipment to the scene. Wherever practicable, exercises should involve the Fire Service and other sources of assistance.

All estate staff should know what to do if they come across a fire. The most useful general rules are:

1. If you see a fire starting, tackle it.
2. If after a few minutes it is clearly beyond your control (i.e. if it is extending) leave it and report immediately to:
   a. The Fire Service (Dial 999).
   b. The Estate Fire Control Centre.
   c. If there are two or more of you, one should run to report the fire whilst the rest tackle the blaze.

Calling out fire fighting teams

Whenever a report of a fire is received the Fire Service and the Police should be informed immediately, giving whatever details are known of its location, type and size. As speed of response is vital the Fire Service should be informed even if the report is only of suspicious smoke which needs further investigation. If the report proves to be a false alarm any Fire Service tender on route can usually be recalled to base by radio.

The man in charge on the estate should gather as many men as he can find quickly and hasten to the fire with the fire fighting equipment. He should not wait to muster a large gang as fires can grow rapidly and a few determined hands soon at the scene can be far more effective than a score or more half an hour later. The rest of the staff should be under instructions to go at once to the fire by the best available means. Some kind of audible warning such as a siren, hunting horn or a loud whistle may be of help depending on the size of the estate and the scatter of the workforce.

Fire plans

Plan layout

Once an owner has assessed the fire danger on his estate as a whole and in each compartment block of woodland and has decided on the fire precautions he will take and on the arrangements for fire fighting, he should set out the details in a fire plan. This will be useful for keeping the matter under review and for advising all who will be involved with fire protection measures. On a small estate the whole plan, including maps, may be no more than a few sheets which can be used in the field under emergency conditions. Larger estates, however, may consider having two plans: an organisation plan and an emergency plan. The format would be a planning document setting out prescriptions, organisation, responsibilities and non-emergency procedures whereas the latter would be restricted to information needed in a fire emergency and would be made accessible at all times.

10 Wind

Many of Britain's plantation forests have been established on high elevation sites mainly in the north and west of the country where wind exposure levels and cold wet soils are serious site limitations which can frequently reduce tree growth rates and lead to shortened crop rotations as a result of the progressive spread of windthrow. Such progressive wind blow on sites with restricted root development is termed *endemic windthrow* and results from normal winter gales. Up to a point the occurrence of endemic windthrow can be predicted and its effects minimised by appropriate silvicultural action and planning. In contrast, *catastrophic windthrow* damage is much less predictable and results from the more infrequent severe storms which can devastate forests and woodlands with both good and restricted root development. The great storms of 16 October 1987 and 25 January 1990 were outstanding examples of such catastrophic and unpredictable damage.

This chapter is principally concerned with managing plantations where high windspeeds regularly occur. Wind affects forests in two main ways. Firstly, under prolonged exposure to persistent high winds tree growth rates are reduced and the stem form changes. In very extreme conditions of wind exposure young trees may die as a result of severe tissue desiccation and mechanical abrasion. Secondly, semi-mature plantations particularly on exposed upland sites where wet or compacted soils restrict root development, are susceptible to premature windthrow during the frequent winter gales which occur in such areas.

Management responses to wind

In order to make sensible forecasts of production it is necessary to predict rates of tree growth and risks of windthrow at various heights on exposed sites and several techniques have been developed for this purpose. It is often necessary to adopt particular silvicultural practices on sites where windspeeds are critical so as to minimise growth restrictions and increase plantation stability. Improved prediction of windthrow susceptibility enables more accurate production forecasting and resource planning. The adoption of effective preventive measures against windthrow is highly desirable to ensure maximum rotation length and increase yields of the more valuable sawlog material at the time of clear felling.

Surveys

As a first step in dealing with the problem of protection against wind damage it is desirable to carry out assessments to determine the severity of exposure of the site and the following two main methods are commonly employed.

Topex assessment

This is a method which indicates the degree of site exposure based on the amount of shelter given to the area by surrounding high ground. Skyline angles for the eight major compass points are measured by a clinometer or Abney level and totalled to produce a Topex score which allows the site to be classified into one of five exposure classes ranging from shel-

K.F. Miller and **C.P. Quine,** Silviculture (North) Branch

tered to severely exposed. Topex surveys are useful in assessing the afforestation potential of bare land and are also necessary in predicting the windthrow susceptibility of forest areas.

Exposure flag surveys

These involve the use of special cotton flags distributed over the assessment site covering a representative range of site elevation and aspect. The cotton material slowly erodes away from the free edge of the flag at a rate which is dependent on the wind exposure level present at a flag site. Differences in site exposure over an extensive area are reflected in the different rates of flag attrition. Increased elevation leads to increased rates of flag attrition and

Tatter flag.

forest managers can determine the approximate elevation limits for economic tree planting from an exposure flag survey. When wind exposure on any site gives flag attrition rates in excess of 12–13 cm^2 per day, tree growth rates are likely to be depressed below yield class 6 and such sites would not normally be considered suitable for commercial afforestation. A typical exposure flag survey on a 500 ha area will require the deployment of between 10 and 20 flags. Worn flags are replaced and assessed every 2 months and the whole survey should run for 2–3 years to cover the effect of annual variations in exposure levels.

Although flag attrition generally increases with elevation, the rate of increase changes in different geographical locations. In particular the more exposed north and west of Britain exhibits increases in flag attrition with small rises in elevation compared with the less windy southern and eastern parts of the country. It has been possible to divide Britain into 7 wind zones based on the rate of flag attrition with elevation. This wind zonation is shown in Figure 10.1 and is an important factor in assessing the windthrow susceptibility of forest areas.

The serious economic losses associated with endemic windthrow make it important for forest managers to be able to predict where and when windthrow is likely to occur and to select the most appropriate silvicultural and management treatments to delay or restrict the incidence of windthrow in plantations.

Windthrow hazard classification

To assist windthrow prediction in British forestry a windthrow hazard classification has been developed as described in Forestry Commission Leaflet 85 *Windthrow hazard classification* and Forestry Commission Occasional Paper 25 *A new series of wind-*

throw monitoring areas in upland Britain. The classification involves assessing four separate site factors allocating a score to each and using the total score to allocate one of six windthrow hazard classes to the forest area:

Windzone + Elevation + Topex + Soil

=

Combined score

=

Windthrow hazard class

Each windthrow hazard class is associated with a *critical height* which is the standard top height at which windthrow is likely to start and a *terminal*

Wind snap.

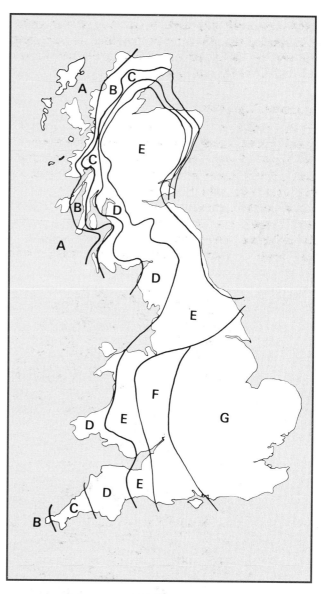

FIGURE 10.1 Wind zonation map of Great Britain, based on a combination of windspeed data and exposure flag surveys. (Equal gradation of wind exposure from high **A** to low **G**.)

Table 10.1

Windthrow hazard class	Critical heights (m) (onset of windthrow)			Estimated terminal heights (m) (40% stand area blown)		
	Non-thin	Selective thin	Systematic thin	Non-thin	Selective thin	Systematic thin
1	Unconstrained by windthrow					
2	25.0	22.0	21.0	31.0	28.0	28.0
3	22.0	19.0	17.0	27.0	25.0	23.5
4	19.0	16.0	14.0	24.0	21.5	18.5
5	16.0	13.0	12.0	19.5	17.5	15.5
6	13.0	10.0	9.0	15.5	13.5	11.5

height which is the standard top height when windthrow has spread progressively to reach the 40% damage level and clear felling would become necessary. Critical and terminal heights are influenced by thinning practice and the interaction is summarised in Table 10.1.

As can be seen from Table 10.1 the thinning generally leads to the commencement of windthrow at lower top heights (and earlier ages) than in unthinned stands and systematic thinning (line or chevron patterns) is worse than selective thinning. In addition the timing and intensity of thinning will also influence windthrow.

It is important to appreciate that actual critical and terminal heights observed in any single forest location may deviate widely from the figure shown in Table 10.1. The critical heights shown can be supported by field validation surveys but the terminal heights are only approximate and the rate of spread of windthrow is highly variable. As a general rule stands in the highly susceptible windthrow classes 5 and 6 should be left unthinned. For those in the most stable hazard classes 1 and 2, the manager is free to choose any normal thinning technique and stands can usually be grown to full economic rotation

without difficulty. In the intermediate hazard classes 3 and 4 thinning options are more limited and care must be taken over the timing, pattern and intensity of thinning to avoid precipitating the onset of serious windthrow.

Because the windthrow hazard classification and derived critical and terminal heights are very broad approximations that cannot be applied safely to individual stands in the forest the main purpose of the classification is the zonation of extensive forest areas as an aid to general decisions on thinning policy and to production forecasting. Decisions on felling or thinning of individual compartments and stands will be subject to a range of additional constraints and objectives.

The clearance of windthrow pockets and normal clear felling operations can also carry an increased risk of windthrow spreading in surrounding forests by exposing unstable edges of plantations to the full force of the wind. It is recommended that in the clearance of windthrown pockets leaning edges should be left intact and clear felling operations should be planned to avoid leaving susceptible forest margins (see Chapter 17 'Planning for the second rotation').

Harvesting windthrown trees.

143

Reducing the risk of windthrow

Site preparation and soil type are important influences on the incidence and extent of windthrow. In particular, spaced furrow ploughing can result in restrictions to root spread with the main structural roots tending to align along the plough ridge and being unable to cross the open furrow. Double mould board ploughing is likely to produce less serious root restriction than single mould board ploughing since there are fewer open furrows per hectare and the more gently sloping sides of the ridges and furrows may encourage increased development of structural rooting at these points. On the drier podzols and ironpan soils complete ploughing may promote improved root architecture. On the wet gley soils sub-surface drainage by mole ploughing with shallow surface cultivation or mounding are attractive alternatives to spaced furrow ploughing for improved rooting and stability.

Silvicultural treatment

Spacing or respacing of plantations can be expected to influence windthrow susceptibility to some extent mainly through their effect on tree shape. The use of wide spacing at planting or subsequent respacing treatment will encourage development of heavily tapered individual tree stems which may resist wind loading more effectively than close grown stems with lower taper. However, any benefits of improved individual resistance to wind loading from more tapered stems may well be counteracted by the increased canopy roughness which will generate higher turbulence levels above the forest. The deeper tree crowns in widely spaced stands will also permit deeper wind penetration and in combination with increased turbulence the wind loading on individual stems will increase. In addition, widely planted stems will suffer from a reduction in timber quality

Wind tunnel experiments using model trees.

Airflow research at
Rivox in south Scotland.

(due to increased branch size, branch retention and
large juvenile core) which reduces the attractiveness
of this option even further. Other silvicultural options such as pre-commercial thinning or chemical
thinning of plantations have potential application on
high windthrow hazard class sites where conventional thinning is undesirable. Provided the operations are carried out well before critical height,
stability should not be impaired and timber quality
is unlikely to be prejudiced. Self-thinning mixtures
of pine and spruce are also a useful option for high
hazard class sites.

Current windthrow research

Current research at the Forestry Commission's
Northern Research Station (Table 10.2) aims to improve the prediction of wind damage and to recom-
mend ways in which damage can be prevented. This
requires an understanding of the complex interactions between wind climate, site and forest. Past
research by the Forestry Commission has concentrated upon prediction of damage and has been
largely empirical in nature. This work is continuing
but is now supplemented by a strong fundamental

145

Table 10.2   Current windthrow research programmes of the Forestry Commission

Scale of relevance	Study	Measurements
Tree	Aeromechanics	Actual canopy airflow, tree movement, forces.
	Root/soil strength	Responses to dynamic loading.
	Root/water-table	Variation in root strength and depth.
	Root/site preparation	Variation in root morphology and spread.
	Wind tunnel studies	Canopy airflow and forces on model trees.
Forest	Wind tunnel studies	Airflow with different tree/coupe patterns.
	Airflow studies	Airflow modification by topography and forests.
	Windthrow monitoring areas	Damage occurrence, causes and progression.
National	Windthrow monitoring areas	Damage related to forest type, wind climate
	Wind climate of Britain	Regional windiness variability.

research programme to improve understanding of the mechanics of windthrow and to allow preventive measures to be formulated. Research is progressing across a wide range of spatial scales, from studies of individual trees to studies of national wind climate.

The tree scale experiments mentioned above aim to elucidate the interaction between individual trees and the wind, and individual root systems with the soil/site. At the forest scale the wind-tunnel, airflow and windthrow monitoring studies all seek to explain/predict where damage will occur – the first two studies pay specific attention to airflow, while the third seeks to integrate all the potential factors. The work needs to be placed within a national framework particularly with respect to the wind climate of Great Britain. The windthrow monitoring areas, by representing different regional types, can be used to understand damage at the national scale. Anemometers located at each monitoring site provide an opportunity for studying the wind climate of upland Britain.

Anemometers in place over 11 m high Sitka spruce plantation.

11 Management for timber production

This chapter is divided into four parts: the first deals with the management of a forest enterprise; the second describes some of the needs and methods of data collection for forest management; the third deals with the planning, organisation and control of production; the final part deals with forest mensuration.

Management

Successful management is the result of careful planning, organisation and control of all forest operations to fulfil the policy objectives of the owner. Management involves choosing between two or more possible courses of action and comprises three main functions:

1. setting the objectives of the enterprise;
2. planning the organising operations;
3. controlling operations.

Policy

The major objectives of the forest enterprise should be established in a statement of policy. The objectives are the criteria used by managers when choosing between alternative courses of action and by which the success of management is judged. An organisation can expect objectives to change and forest management should be sufficiently flexible to meet this. Only when the objectives have been clearly stated with an order of priorities can the best method of achieving them be worked out.

Planning

Planning is the task of organising the forest operations to achieve the policy objectives. It comprises three main phases:

1. collection of data;
2. analysis of the various possible courses of action;
3. the formulation of plans.

Long-term plans should reflect the long-term policy objectives of the forest enterprise. They should only be altered when a fundamental change in the environment affecting the enterprise has been recognised.

Medium-term plans will usually be in the form of 5-year forecasts of work. They will deal with quantities of work but not locations and they should be prepared at the forest rather than the individual stand level.

Short-term plans will usually be prepared to cover a single year's operation. They will deal with quantities and locations of work by compartments or sub-compartments for all forest operations. As such they become the annual programmes of work and thus form the basis of the annual budget. They should take account of the immediate circumstances and will be subject to constant modification.

Control

Control of all operations ensures that short-term plans are implemented. Control is exercised by checking the progress of work weekly or monthly

T.J.D. Rollinson, former Head of Mensuration Branch

throughout the budget period and adjusting the allocation of resources as necessary. Automatic data processing using computers allows managers to review budget decisions quickly and effectively. Consideration needs to be given at the time of plan preparation to the type and quantity of data that will be received by managers at all levels of the enterprise and also how the data are to be collected, processed and distributed.

Data collection

The first step in planning is to describe the forest resource qualitatively and quantitatively. This involves the collection and analysis of data. Without this it is impossible to evaluate the results of future actions and hence impossible to judge which course of action is most likely to fulfil the objectives of the enterprise. Forest surveys may be undertaken for many purposes but it is usually necessary to know the legal boundaries of the forest estate, the area distribution of stands by species, age class, stocking and yield class, and the roading layout.

Although all activities on a single estate interact with one another to some extent, the critical element concerns the management of the growing stock of trees. From this flows the requirement to find markets, to programme replanting following felling, to design a system of access routes for general management purposes and for harvesting, etc. In view of this central concern with the growing stock, it is natural that surveys and the records derived from them should concentrate on composition of the growing stock and the following sections therefore deal with this aspect.

There are other kinds of survey which may be found necessary. The assessment of windthrow risk is one, the method for which is described in Chapter 10. At the time of replanting after felling and before new planting is undertaken, a soil survey will often be of assistance in deciding on species, cultivation and drainage. Surveys designed to serve other objectives than timber production are often required, for example to provide the best layout for pheasant shoots, to record interesting wildlife habitats including species lists and to evaluate the demand for informal recreation provided by a picnic place.

Planning of growing stock surveys

The essential data required and standards of collection must be decided before planning the survey. Data from earlier surveys, planting and felling records, compartment schedules and forest histories will provide a useful guide to the survey intensity required. A preliminary reconnaissance enables the manager to make an assessment of the broad nature of crop classification required and will give an indication of the value of existing records available. There are two main ways of recording forest survey information, firstly on a map and secondly on a manual or automatic data retrieval system.

Administrative divisions

The basic management unit of a forest is the stand or sub-compartment. This is described as being an area comprising a more or less homogeneous crop in terms of age, species composition and condition. Sub-compartments are not necessarily permanent units of management since they will probably change as the forest develops through felling, restocking, etc. Sub-compartments are sub-divisions of compartments delineated on a basic forest map. Compartments are permanent management units and their boundaries should be permanent and clearly defined on the ground. They should as far as possible be based upon the forest road systems and other well defined features such as streams, paths or other natural features. The size of the compartments will depend upon a number of factors including the terrain, the intensity of working and the size of the forest.

Forest maps

The first step in the preparation of any management plan for a forest enterprise is to define the extent of the area under management. The external boundaries of the area should be marked on basic planning and record maps. The map is required for day to day planning of operations and to find the way around the forest.

In the Forestry Commission, Ordnance Survey 1:10 000 scale sheets are used as the basic maps but 1:25 000 scale O.S. maps may be a convenient and complementary base for broad brush planning in large forests. Internal crop boundaries should be identified and mapped whenever possible direct from air photos, when a minimum of ground check will be necessary to confirm their validity.

Maps should generally be sufficiently accurate to measure the area of individual stands to at least the nearest 0.5 ha. It is often convenient to prepare a basic map of the forest based on O.S. sheets, showing permanent features such as streams and rivers, rides, roads and boundaries, from which transparencies may be prepared to provide the basis for stock, road and other management maps. It should be noted however that O.S. hold the copyright to all their maps and their permission must be obtained before copies are taken from them. Over-complicated maps should be avoided. Stock maps will show road lines which form compartment or sub-compartment boundaries, but it will usually be more convenient and less confusing to show road classification, bridges, culverts, and proposed road lines on a separate roads map. Figure 11.1 shows an example of a Forestry Commission stock map.

Data recording

There are no generally accepted standard forms for data recording. The design of forms or schedules depends upon the information to be collected and on the way it is to be stored and presented. Automatic data processing on computers allows management data to be stored and summarised in a wide variety of ways, but it may still be desirable to retain some form of manual data retrieval system, unless access to the computer is fast enough for local operational use.

Aerial photography

The availability of up-to-date good quality photo cover* has radically altered the approach to forest survey and crop inventory. Survey and inventory design should combine air photo interpretation with ground checks requiring only the use of fairly simple equipment. Where up-to-date photography is available, features can often be transferred directly on to the base map within a framework of known ground control points. When scale differences between plots and basic map are small, this task can be done by means of a scale rule or proportional dividers.

Vertical photographs are essential for basic mapping and for crop interpretation. Panchromatic black and white film is normally adequate for general inventory work, preferably used as stereo pairs. Ideal photo scales are 1:10 000 for ground work and 1:20 000 for machine plotting but scales of 1:7500 to 1:25 000 are acceptable where photo cover already exists.

With practice and some elementary training, relatively inexperienced surveyors can readily learn to

---

*Central registers of aerial cover are held at Ordnance Survey, Southampton and at Scottish Development Department, Edinburgh for Scottish cover.

use stereoscopes to identify tree crops in air photos. The major tree genera, if not the species, can be seen on good quality air photographs at 1:10 000 or larger scales. These instruments enable the surveyor to construct a three dimensional image from a pair of adjacent overlapping photographs. Cheap pocket stereoscopes can be used in the forest with a pair of photographs mounted on a clipboard. The more expensive table or mirror stereoscopes give a fuller view of the stereoscopic model, thus speeding up interpretation work, but they cannot be used in the field.

At 1:10 000 or larger scale, the proportions of species in mixtures, stocking densities, blank areas and canopy cover in two-storeyed crops are more readily and accurately measured from aerial photos than from ground survey. The ages of crops are generally obtained from records, but may be estimated by whorl or ring counts where they are not otherwise available, or where extensive and late beating up has taken place.

Where suitable photographs are not available, 35 mm photography, taken from a light aircraft by hand-held or fixed mounted camera, can be quite cheap provided the pilot and photographer have had some experience. The photography will probably be unsuitable for basic mapping, but can be invaluable for sketching in sub-compartments within reliably mapped compartmentation.

Where air photos are not available it is seldom worth conducting detailed surveys on the ground. Adequate sub-compartmentation can be achieved by pacing, combined where possible with sketch mapping from adjacent hillsides. Where there are considerable height variations and/or stocking densities between adjacent groups which are too small to map individually, arbitrary grouping may be necessary by applying average crop features to the whole sub-compartment.

Additional data

Additional surveys to provide management information may be required, for example on the assessment of disease occurrence or damage, the estimation of growth rates, the assessment of risk of windthrow, planning road alignments or estimating the need for cultural operations such as draining and fertilising.

Planning, organising and controlling the production of wood

The principal objectives of any forest enterprise are likely to depend upon the composition, growth and yield of the growing stock. Control of the growing stock is achieved by applying specified cutting regimes to the forest. Certain basic information is required when making decisions about the cutting regimes to adopt. Knowledge of the area, age and species composition of the crops is essential, together with some information about the standing volume and rate of growth of each stand. Rates of growth are conventionally defined through yield classes as described below. With this information available a manager is able to plan, organise and control the cutting regimes and to forecast the supply of timber and thus to adopt an appropriate marketing strategy.

The following paragraphs explain how to forecast production, describe the yield class system, give guidance on the choice of cutting regimes, describe the various factors which constitute a thinning regime and consider how to control the thinning and felling yields.

Forecasting production

Forecasts of future volume production are essential for market planning, for the planning of labour and machinery resources and to provide the basis for the

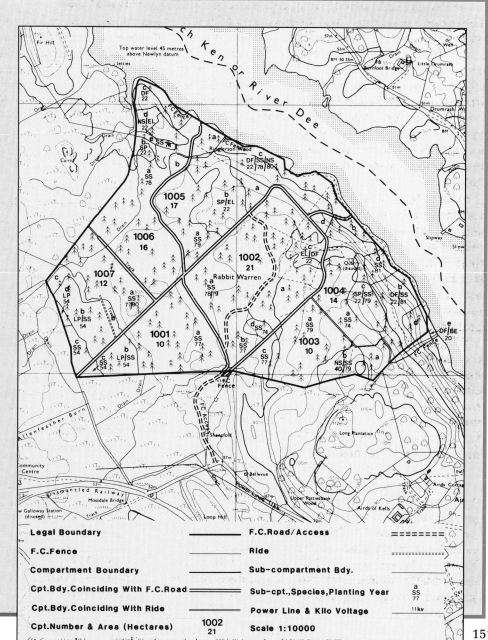

FIGURE 11.1 Part of a Forestry Commission stock map.

Legal Boundary

F.C.Fence

Compartment Boundary

Cpt.Bdy.Coinciding With F.C.Road

Cpt.Bdy.Coinciding With Ride

Cpt.Number & Area (Hectares)   1002 / 21

F.C.Road/Access

Ride

Sub-compartment Bdy.

Sub-cpt.,Species,Planting Year   a / SS / 77

Power Line & Kilo Voltage   11kv

Scale 1:10000

151

valuation of growing stock. To forecast production it is necessary to know:

- the present condition of the forest (inventory);
- the pattern of present and future growth (yield class);
- the thinning and felling proposals (cutting regimes).

Forecasts of production from the forest are calculated by totalling the forecasts of production from each stand within a forest. For each stand the following information is needed: species, age, yield class, area, past treatment including plant spacing, and proposed future treatment. The species and age are relatively easy to discover. The assessment of yield class is discussed in Forestry Commission Booklet 48 *Yield models for forest management*. Accurate maps are required to determine the area and it is most important that this is the area of fully stocked forest, excluding roads, rides and any other unproductive areas such as ponds. Finally, details of past treatments and the proposed future treatments are needed to select the most appropriate yield model. The expected volume and other stand characteristics at each thinning can be read directly from the yield model and the figures for the felling can be calculated by combining the figures for the thinning at that age with the main crop after thinning at the same age. The volume estimates are for one hectare so they must be multiplied by the area to give the figure for the whole stand. Mixtures or two-storeyed stands are most conveniently dealt with by separating the component species or storeys and deriving an effective net area of each based on the proportion of the canopy it occupies.

The forecast thinning and felling volumes can be separated into volumes of large timber to stated top diameters and volumes of smaller timber, using Stand Assortment Tables. Their use is discussed in

detail in Forestry Commission Booklet 39 *Forest mensuration handbook*. Further tables based on wide spacing and for no thin stands are available in Forestry Commission Booklet 48.

The Yield Class system

In an even-aged stand the cumulative volume production, including dead trees and thinnings, divided

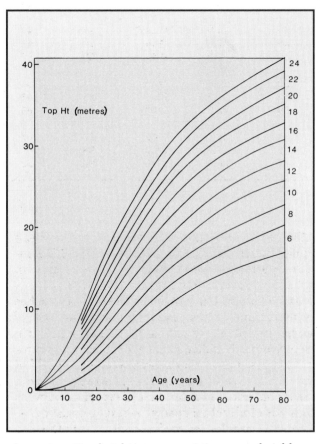

FIGURE 11.2 Top height/age curve giving general yield classes for Sitka spruce.

Table 11.1 Yield model for unthinned Sitka spruce, YC 12, 2.0 m spacing

Age (years)	Top height (m)	No. of trees /ha	Mean dbh (cm)	Basal area /ha (m²)	Mean volume (m³)	Volume /ha (m³)	Per cent mortality	Mean Annual Increment volume/ha (m³)
20	7.3	2309	11	24	0.03	66	0	3.3
25	10.0	2249	14	34	0.06	133	0	5.3
30	12.5	2123	16	43	0.10	214	1	7.1
35	14.9	1911	18	49	0.16	301	2	8.6
40	17.2	1714	20	54	0.23	386	3	9.7
45	19.2	1547	22	58	0.30	465	5	10.3
50	21.0	1405	23	61	0.38	534	6	10.7
55	22.5	1293	25	63	0.46	593	8	10.8
60	23.7	1209	26	65	0.53	642	9	10.7
65	24.8	1145	27	67	0.60	683	10	10.5
70	25.7	1092	28	68	0.66	718	11	10.3
75	26.5	1046	29	70	0.72	751	12	10.0

by the age of the stand, is referred to as the Mean Annual Increment (MAI). After planting, MAI increases during the early years of vigorous growth, reaches a maximum, and then declines with increasing age. The point at which the MAI curve reaches the maximum is the maximum average rate of volume increment which a particular stand can achieve, and this indicates the yield class. For example, a stand capable of a maximum MAI of 14 m³ per hectare has a yield class of 14. The range of yield classes commonly encountered in British conditions varies with individual species and may be as low as 4 for many broadleaves, and as high as 30 in the case of some conifers. When assessing the yield class it is possible to avoid the measurement or prediction of cumulative volume production because there is a good relationship between top height and cumulative volume production of a stand. The relationship allows yield class to be read directly from top height/age curves. An example of the top height/age curve for Sitka spruce is shown in Figure 11.2.

Yield class obtained through top height and age of the stand alone is termed General Yield Class (GYC). Yield class obtained from some measure or prediction of the actual mean annual volume increment of the stand is termed Local Yield Class (LYC). Where LYC is known it should be used in preference to GYC. The assessment of General and Local Yield Class is described in Forestry Commission Booklet 48.

Cutting regimes

Yield models have been prepared for all the major forest species in Britain and for a wide variety of treatments including a range of initial spacings and thinning treatments, including no thinning. They are available with Forestry Commission Booklet 48. These models are tabular presentations of stand growth and yield. Table 9 is an example of the yield model for Sitka spruce, Yield Class 12, unthinned, planted at 2.0 m spacing. The models can be used to compare the results of alternative treatments before deciding how to manage a particular stand or group of stands, and to forecast future thinning and felling yields.

Thinning

Thinning is the removal of a proportion of the trees in a crop. It is usually practised in order to provide more growing space for the remaining trees, to increase the total yield of usable timber over the life of the stand, and to provide an intermediate yield of timber. It affects the growth and yield of stands, their size class distribution, quality and stability. These factors need to be translated into economic terms. A policy of no thinning may be desirable on windy sites or where early thinnings are difficult to work and sell profitably. The various factors which constitute a thinning regime are considered separately below and in more detail in Forestry Commission Field Book 2 *Thinning control*.

Thinning type

Thinnings may be selective or systematic. A *selective* thinning is one in which trees are removed or retained on their individual merits. In *low* thinning, trees are removed predominantly from the lower canopy, that is the suppressed and sub-dominant trees. In *crown* thinning trees are removed predomi-nantly from the upper canopy, that is some dominants and co-dominants, with the aim of giving selected dominants freedom to grow rapidly. The commonest type of selective thinning is known as *intermediate* thinning. It involves removal of most of the suppressed and sub-dominant trees and also opening up the canopy by breaking up groups of competing dominant and co-dominant trees so as to encourage the development of the better trees and to leave an open and fairly uniform stand.

Systematic thinning is a thinning in which trees are removed according to a predetermined system, such as line thinning, which does not permit selection according to the merits of individual trees. Systematic thinning is usually cheaper and easier to manage than selective thinning but the operation may leave parts of the crop unthinned and may result in losses of volume production and reduced stand stability. Systematic thinning should only be considered where the saving in cost is greater than the likely loss of future revenue.

Thinning intensity

The thinning intensity is the rate at which volume is removed, for example 10 m^3 per hectare per year. The maximum thinning intensity which can be maintained without causing a loss of cumulative volume production over the rotation is known as the marginal thinning intensity. For most species this critical intensity assessed from the time of first thinning is about 70 per cent of the yield class per year. The marginal thinning intensity is often chosen but there are circumstances when it will not be the best choice. If thinnings are difficult to sell, thinning may not be undertaken or a lower thinning intensity adopted. If large sized trees are required as soon as possible, a higher thinning intensity may be adopted even though total volume production will be reduced.

Thinning cycle

The thinning cycle is the interval in years between successive thinnings. Long cycles involve heavier single thinnings which are usually more profitable but may increase the risk of windthrow and in extreme cases they may result in some loss of volume production. The usual length of thinning cycle is from 4–6 years in young or fast growing crops, and about 10 years for older or slower growing crops.

Thinning yield

The thinning yield is the actual volume removed in any one thinning. If a fully stocked stand is thinned at the marginal thinning intensity, the thinning yield will be 70 per cent of the yield class, multiplied by the cycle. For example, the annual thinning yield for a stand of Yield Class 14 being thinned at the marginal thinning intensity on a 5-year cycle is: $70\% \times 14 \times 5 = 49$ m^3 per hectare.

The thinning yield should not be so heavy that it opens up a stand to the risk of windthrow or to invasion by other woody species, and thinning should not take all the dominant and good quality trees so that none is left to form a reasonable crop after thinning.

Other considerations

The treatment of understocked and overstocked stands, mixtures, uneven aged stands, diseased stands with patchy growth or partial check, and treatment of line thinning are dealt with in Forestry Commission Field Book 2 *Thinning control.*

Field procedure for thinning

Inspection racks should be cut at intervals throughout the plantation to assess the need for thinning. With selective thinning it will usually be necessary to undertake a measure of brashing, that is the removal of the lower branches to head height, to gain access to view the trees and to mark those to be cut. It is an expensive operation however, and even in selective thinning it is rarely justifiable to brash every tree. Brashing is usually unnecessary with row thinning as only the end trees in each row to be removed need to be marked. Marking may be done with paint, a timber scribe or more conventionally by cutting a blaze on the side of a tree with a slasher. If it is decided to mark trees that are to be retained, paint should be used. With selective thinning every tree selected should be marked on at least two sides so that it is possible to' see from every angle which trees have been chosen for removal. Having decided on the thinning treatment which will yield the maximum benefit, it is essential to exercise some measure of control in order that these aims and long-term plans may be realised.

Yield control

The felling yield is determined by the area of felling and the standing volume per unit area. The detailed application of a yield control system is relatively straightforward if the annual programme of production is drawn up stand by stand and if the progress of work in terms of both area and volume is recorded alongside the planned cut. Control of felling is achieved by keeping a cumulative record of the volume cut and comparing this at intervals with the planned yield for the same period. With thinning yields it may be necessary to supplement the retrospective form of control using records of production with another form of control which can be exercised at the marking stage before the trees are cut. Failure to control the volume removed as thinnings can result in overcutting which leads to a loss in volume production, or undercutting which de-

THINNING BROADLEAVED STANDS

Thinning of broadleaved trees differs in some important respects from thinning of conifers. This is due mainly to the greater variety of stem form found in broadleaved stands and in thinning broadleaves the emphasis is on selection for quality rather than yield management. Thinning should aim to produce well balanced, even crowns on final crop trees. Any poor quality trees, particularly if vigorous, must be removed at an early stage. The danger in leaving them is that they create large gaps when finally removed and unbalanced crowns later in the rotation on final crop trees.

Except in strip mixtures and for first thinnings of very dense plantations, mechanical and systematic thinning methods, e.g. removal of 1 in 4 rows, generally have no place in thinning broadleaves. The need to favour the well formed trees present takes precedence over the need to open up a stand in a systematic way. However, systematic establishment of racks is needed in order to minimise extraction damage.

Selecting which trees to favour is the most important part in thinning broadleaves. This selection is best done in winter when the condition of the upper stem and crown is more easily seen. For most species the following criteria apply:

- Good stem form and freedom from defect on the lower bole.
- Absence of deep forking in crown which increases risk of storm damage and eventual loss of tree.
- Good vigour.
- Freedom from defect in upper stem and crown, e.g. squirrel damage, evidence of disease.
- Low incidence of epicormic branching.

For broadleaves the importance of achieving a particular level of thinning intensity is less important than in conifers because the primary purpose of thinning is to favour the final crop trees rather than maximise total production per hectare. Because thinning broadleaves seeks to produce a final crop of relatively few but well formed trees one option is to attempt to identify such trees at an early stage and to favour these by very heavy thinning. However, this system has its limitations as in most stands there are usually few trees of good form which restricts the choice of ones to favour in thinning. Also, many broadleaved species do not have strong apical dominance and heavy thinning may depress height increment and encourage the development of spreading heavily branched crowns. Heavy thinnings may stimulate epicormic branching especially in oak and poplar. *Note:* summer thinning of broadleaves may help to reduce epicormic branching.

Mixtures

Thinning of mixtures is essential if the final crop species grows more slowly than others in the stand, a common feature of broadleaved/conifer crops. Thinning secures the final crop species and prevents trees becoming over-topped, suppressed, or slender and whippy. Neglect or delay in thinning is more serious in mixed than in pure stands since one species eventually tends to dominate. The principles of early selection of potential final crop trees, priority removal of mis-shaped trees and the timing cycle of the thinnings are substantially the same as for pure stands. Thinning intensity in terms of yield per hectare per year should be determined separately for each major species component of a stand. The secondary species in a mixture is mostly removed by about the fourth thinning, i.e. by about half to two-thirds of the way through the rotation of the final crop species, though a few specimens may be retained for amenity and added value.

Thinning mixtures of broadleaves is relatively straightforward favouring good stems of main crop species and early removal of mis-shaped trees. Where intermediate yields of good quality cherry, sycamore and/or ash are sought from mixtures with beech and/or oak, some favouring in early thinnings of both the short rotation and the long rotation species will be necessary.

Spacing experiment in Sitka spruce – mid-Scotland.

Table 11.2 Tariff numbers

Top height (m)	SP	CP	LP	SS	NS	EL	JL/HL	DF	WH	RC	GF	NF	Oak	Birch	
8.0	17	16	15	16	16	14	16	15	17	14	14	14	16	14	Subtract 1
8.5	17	16	16	16	17	15	16	16	17	14	15	15	17	14	from the
9.0	18	17	16	17	18	15	17	16	18	15	16	16	17	15	tariff
9.5	18	18	17	18	18	16	18	17	19	15	16	16	18	15	number
10.0	19	18	18	18	19	17	18	17	19	16	17	17	18	16	for inter-
10.5	19	19	19	19	19	18	19	18	20	16	18	18	19	16	mediate
11.0	20	20	19	19	20	18	20	18	20	17	18	18	19	17	and low
11.5	20	20	20	20	20	19	20	19	21	17	19	19	20	17	selective
12.0	21	21	21	21	21	20	21	20	22	18	20	20	20	17	thinning
12.5	21	22	21	21	22	20	22	20	22	18	20	21	21	18	
13.0	22	23	22	22	22	21	22	21	23	19	21	21	21	18	**Oak**
13.5	22	23	23	23	23	22	23	21	24	19	22	22	22	19	Use also for
14.0	23	24	24	23	23	22	24	22	24	20	23	23	22	19	beech,
14.5	24	25	24	24	24	23	24	22	25	21	23	23	23	20	ash, elm,
15.0	24	25	25	24	24	24	25	23	25	21	24	24	23	20	alder and
15.5	25	26	26	25	25	25	26	24	26	22	25	25	24	21	sweet
16.0	25	27	26	26	26	25	26	24	27	22	25	25	24	21	chestnut
16.5	26	27	27	26	26	26	27	25	27	23	26	26	25	22	
17.0	26	28	28	27	27	27	28	25	28	23	27	27	25	22	**Birch**
17.5	27	29	28	27	27	27	29	26	28	24	27	27	25	22	Use also for
18.0	27	30	29	28	28	28	29	26	29	24	28	28	26	23	sycamore
18.5	28	30	30	29	29	29	30	27	30	25	29	29	26	23	and poplar
19.0	28	31	31	29	29	29	31	28	30	25	29	29	27	24	
19.5	29	32	31	30	30	30	31	28	31	26	30	30	27	24	
20.0	29	32	32	30	30	31	32	29	31	26	31	31	28	25	
20.5	30	33	33	31	31	31	33	29	32	27	31	31	28	25	
21.0	30	34	33	32	31	32	33	30	33	27	32	32	28	25	
21.5	31	34	34	32	32	33	34	30	33	28	33	33	29	26	
22.0	31	35	35	33	33	34	35	31	34	29	34	33	29	26	
22.5	32	36	36	33	33	34	35	31	35	29	34	34	30	27	
23.0	32	37	36	34	34	35	36	32	35	30	35	35	30	27	
23.5	33	37	37	35	34	36	37	33	36	30	36	35	30	27	
24.0	33	38	38	35	35	36	37	33	36	31	36	36	31	28	
24.5	34	39	38	36	35	37	38	34	37	31	37	37	31	28	
25.0	34	39	39	36	36	38	39	34	38	32	38	37	31	28	
25.5	35	40	40	37	37	38	39	35	38	32	38	38	32	29	
26.0	35	41	40	38	37	39	40	35	39	33	39	39	32	29	
26.5	36	41	41	38	38	40	41	36	39	33	40	39	32	29	

Table 11.2 Tariff numbers *(continued)*

Top height (m)	Species													
	SP	CP	LP	SS	NS	EL	JL/HL	DF	WH	RC	GF	NF	Oak	Birch
27.0	36	42	42	39	38	40	42	37	40	34	40	40	33	30
27.5	37	43	43	39	39	41	42	37	41	34	41	41	33	30
28.0	37	43	43	40	40	42	43	38	41	35	42	41	34	30
28.5	38	44	44	41	40	43	44	38	42	36	42	42	34	31
29.0	38	45	45	41	41	43	44	39	43	36	43	43	34	31
29.5	39	46	45	42	41	44	45	39	43	37	44	43	35	31
30.0	39	46	46	42	42	45	46	40	44	37	44	44	35	32

presses profitability. It may also produce an erratic flow of timber to the consumer. The subject of thinning control is dealt with comprehensively in Forestry Commission Field Book 2 *Thinning control*.

It may be an advantage to divide the forest area into thinning blocks related to the thinning cycle and designed to avoid marked variation in thinning and felling yields from one year to another. The use of thinning blocks is usually necessary unless the area in production is small or there is a relatively limited period of rapidly expanding production.

Crop assessment summaries should give a realistic picture of the growth potential of the forest. Areas which are markedly under or over-stocked or which, owing to delayed early growth, are unlikely to be ready for thinning at the standard age, should be identified individually and their predicted yield modified accordingly. The reliability of forecasts of future yield depends upon:

- the accuracy of the growing stock data;
- the accuracy of the growth predictions;
- the thinning and felling policy being carried out as planned.

Mensuration

This section deals with the measurement of standing and felled timber.

Measurement methods

Measurement of timber is required for several purposes. The most obvious of these is the need to quantify forest produce for sale. Measurement is also required for management, notably for planning purposes and for the control of resources. The measurement of yield class for production forecasting has been described earlier.

There are many different ways of measuring any piece of timber, with inevitable differences in the estimates arrived at. It is thus a fundamental necessity to describe fully the method of measurement and the conventions used in order to convey the full meaning of such estimates. Timber quantity can be expressed in terms of solid volume, stacked volume, green weight, dry weight, length, number of pieces, etc. Traditionally timber quantity has been expressed in terms of solid volume.

Choice of method

Measurement methods are fully described in Forestry Commission Booklet 39 *Forest mensuration handbook* and in Forestry Commission Booklet 49 *Timber measurement – a field guide*. These booklets describe in detail the most commonly used methods for measuring standing and felled timber. The choice of whether the timber should be measured standing or felled depends on who is responsible for the felling and extraction. Where this is done by the buyer the tendency is to measure standing, but if the grower is responsible, felled measure is more usual. However, with small lots of timber, very diverse crops or high value produce such as veneer timber, it may be better to provide a very rough and cheap estimate of standing volume in order to attract the interest of the prospective buyer, but to agree to sell on the basis of an appropriate felled measure.

Simple methods for estimating the volume of a single standing tree, a stand of trees and felled timber are described below. Each of these methods is described in more detail in the publications mentioned above which should be consulted for further information.

Estimating the volume of a standing tree

A rough estimate of the volume of a standing tree can be derived using the following method, based on form factors.

a. Measure the diameter at breast height (dbh) of the tree. The breast height point is the point on the tree at 1.3 m above ground level.

b. Calculate its basal area using the following formula:

$$BA = \frac{\pi \, d^2}{40\,000}$$

where BA = total area in sq m

d = diameter at breast height in cm.

c. Measure the total height of the tree in m.

d. Estimate the form factor of the tree. Use 0.5 for mature conifers in plantations, 0.4 for open grown conifers and 0.35 for younger trees.

e. Multiply the total height by the basal area and by the form factor to give the estimated total volume in cubic metres.

Estimating the volume of a stand

The following method applies to even aged, single species stands. In stands containing a mixture of species or ages, each component of the mixture should be considered separately.

a. Inspect the stand and decide if separate samples are required for different species, ages or crop types. The following steps relate to a single species, age and crop type.

b. From Table 11.3 choose a convenient sample plot

Table 11.3 Radius or side length for various plot sizes

Shape	Length in metres for plot size (ha)						
	0.005	0.01	0.02	0.05	0.10	0.20	0.50
Circular (radius)	4.0	5.6	8.0	12.6	17.8	25.2	39.9
Square (sides)	7.1	10.0	14.1	22.4	31.6	44.7	70.7

Table 11.4 Number of sample plots

Area of stand (ha)	Uniform crop	Variable crop
0.5–2	6	8
2–10	8	12
over 10	10	16

size which will contain between 7 and 20 trees.
c. Decide on the number of plots to be measured from Table 11.4.
d. Select the plots at random. In each plot:
  - measure and record the diameter at breast height of all trees greater than 7 cm dbh;
  - measure and record the total height of the tree of largest dbh within a 5.6 m radius of the plot centre.
e. Calculate the average height of the samples taken in each plot. This gives an estimate of the top height of the stand.

f. Estimate the tariff number of the stand using Table 11.2 for top height/tariff numbers.
g. Calculate the mean dbh using the measurements taken in all plots together. This can be done using a calculator with a square root key as follows:
  - square each dbh;
  - add all the squared values together;
  - divide by the number of trees;
  - calculate the square root, which is the mean dbh.
h. Estimate the mean volume from the mean dbh and tariff numbers which have already been calculated, by using the chart (Figure 11.3).
i. Work out the average number of trees in the plots and divide by the individual plot area to give the estimated number of trees per hectare.
j. Multiply the mean volume by the number of trees per hectare to give the total volume per hectare.
k. Multiply the volume per hectare by the stocked area of the stand to obtain the total volume of the stand.

Measuring felled timber

The traditional method for estimating the volume of sawlogs is the mid diameter method.
a. Measure the length of the log. If the log is longer than 15 m it should be measured in two or more sections.
b. Measure the diameter at the mid point of the log.
c. Calculate the volume of the log using the following formula:

$$V = \frac{\pi d^2 L}{40\ 000}$$

where V = volume in cu m
d = mid diameter in cm
L = length in m.

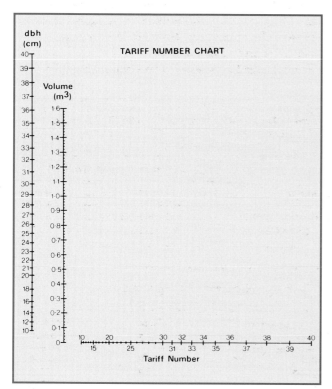

FIGURE 11.3 Tariff number chart.

12 Harvesting

Timber harvesting can be carried out by timber merchants to whom the standing trees have been sold, by specialist firms who do some or all harvesting operations on contract, or by workers employed directly by the forest owner. Modern timber harvesting requires competent planning and a high degree of operator skill, it is not a job for amateurs. Machines such as power saws are highly dangerous in untrained hands. Inadequately planned and poorly executed logging is a certain way to waste money.

Harvesting by direct labour must be on a large enough scale to make it worthwhile training operators, providing adequate equipment and keeping production teams employed all the year round. Few owners of small woodland properties can do this, and they are strongly recommended to use merchants or contractors instead.

On some small estates, woodmen are employed on small-scale harvesting operations at times when no other work is possible. This may be worth doing as a means of keeping men usefully employed, but adequate training in safe working techniques is absolutely essential. Part-time harvesting work seldom allows operators to develop a satisfactory degree of skill, and the financial results are usually disappointing.

Planning

Careful planning is necessary to select the methods best suited to the circumstances of the operation. The most important factors are:

- terrain;
- the forest crop: in particular, tree size, and type of cutting (i.e. thinning, clear felling);
- markets: these determine specification of produce;
- machinery available.

Other factors, such as availability of labour, may also be important.

Terrain

The term 'terrain' is used here to mean land as a working surface. Good knowledge of the forest terrain is the starting point for operational planning. The Forestry Commission uses a classification system based on the three factors of ground conditions, ground roughness and slope. These factors influence the use of machinery in the forest, and the classification system provides a convenient 'shorthand' method of describing working sites. The main features of the system are given in Table 12.1.

The forest crop

In general, harvesting operations are easier and cheaper when trees are large and there is plenty of space to move (clear felling of mature crops is a good example). First thinnings, in contrast, combine small trees and confined working space. They can present considerable difficulty, and the cost of the operations may be greater than the value of the timber produced.

Markets

These govern the specification of products, which in turn influence the harvesting operations. If two or three simple products are required it is possible to

163

the late **A.J.G. Hughes**, and **B.A. Roebuck**, Harvesting and Marketing Division prepare them at stump. Where more products are made, preparation at stump can result in sorting difficulties. Products which demand accurate measurement are best prepared at roadside or, in the case of pitwood, in a depot where working conditions are better.

Machinery

Developments in specialised forest machinery have been rapid in the past decade. Many of the more advanced extraction and processing machines are highly efficient, but their purchase prices are so high that economical operation requires large programmes and intensive use. This precludes many forest owners but some of the larger merchants and contractors are now operating in this field.

Harvesting machinery in general use includes the following:

Chain saws

Lightweight models are most commonly used for conifers and smaller hardwoods.

The chain saw is potentially a very dangerous piece of machinery and it is important that:

a. It is suitable for the use to which it is to be put. Forestry Safety Council guides should be carefully followed.

b. Operators be properly trained. Untrained personnel must *never* be asked or allowed to use chain saws.

c. Correct working methods must be used. Forestry Safety Council guides should be observed.

d. Operators must be properly equipped with protective clothing, as detailed in FSC guides.

e. Saws are regularly serviced and maintained to maker's specifications.

f. Chains are kept sharp and to design specification.

Most of the large manufacturers market a range of saws sufficient to meet the needs of British forestry. Within the overall range of suitable saws the decision as to which to buy will often be influenced by local availability of spare parts and service.

Forwarders

These are tractors which extract timber lifted entirely clear of the ground. The timber is carried on a linked trailer or integral rear bunk. All use a fitted loading crane. The most usual types are:

1. Forwarders consisting of an agricultural tractor of about 60–80 bhp, equipped with safety cab and extra guarding. Drive can be 2-wheel, often with additional band tracks, or 4-wheel, and fitted with a hydraulically operated loading crane. The trailers are usually detachable, 2 or twin-bogie wheeled, with load capacities of 6 to 10 tonnes. Some Scandinavian firms produce a trailer with the crane pillar mounted on the drawbar, so that a suitable farm tractor, or a skidder, can be converted to a forwarder by simply coupling on the trailer unit and the hydraulic connections. The distinguishing feature of this type of forwarder is the absence of any drive to the trailer wheels.

2. Forwarders essentially the same as type 1, but with power drive to the trailer wheels. This can be a mechanical drive from the tractor PTO shaft, or hydraulic drive. A variation of the latter is hydraulic drive to a ribbed wheel mounted centrally above each pair of rear bogie wheels, and which can be brought to drive directly on to the bogie wheels' tyres when traction is required.

3. Purpose-built, frame-steered forwarders, with engine, cab and loader mounted over the front axle or between the front and rear bogie and the load carried over the rear axle or bogie. Engine size generally 80 bhp and above, though some successful smaller models have been produced. Most forwarders have a rear 4-wheel bogie and a single

Organised felling using the bench system.

front axle but some, especially later machines, have a front bogie. All wheels are driven mechanically or hydraulically.

The engine-power requirements for forwarders per tonne of load are less than for other forms of extraction, because the fully-supported load makes for more efficient traction. Ten to 12 bhp per tonne of load is usual. The cross-country ability of modern purpose-built forwarders is equal to other forestry machines on rough and steep ground.

Forwarders use twin bogies to reduce the ground pressure which can be further reduced by fitting band tracks. Wheel chains provide safe grip on difficult ground. Correct tyre choice is important and can reduce the need for band tracks and chains.

Purpose-built forwarders have good ground clearance but some type 1 forwarders are limited by the low position of the trailer drawbar connection which creates difficulties on undulating ground. Forwarders are much more manoeuvrable than is generally realised and have a turning radius as good as other tractors. Purpose-built forwarders have a rotating seat which allows the driver to operate the loader easily, and there are usually dual controls which enable the machine to be moved with the driver facing rearwards.

Choice of loader for a forwarder is important because loader work usually takes up the bulk of working time. Most hydraulic loaders are of the 'knuckleboom' type, consisting of an inner and an outer boom, with a rotatable grapple at the end of the latter. Reach should be at least 4.7 m, and a telescopic extension to the outer boom is an advantage. The size of log to be loaded will determine the lifting torque required: 2.5 tonne-metres is an absolute minimum. Lifting and slewing should be quick and smooth. Good operator training is essential and, in addition, it is worth equipping forwarder loaders with the more efficient E.H.C. 2-lever controls. The grapple should be of the horizontal-cylinder type, preferably full rotating. For general work, a grapple of 0.35 m² jaw area is required, but if loading is nearly all in pulpwood, a special 1.0 m² grapple allows faster work.

The loader can be pillar-mounted behind the cab or on the trailer drawbar but this blocks vision. Another mounting position is on top of a specially strengthened safety cab. Most loaders are pillar mounted. Loaders should not be mounted in front of the cab. Practically all the hydraulic loaders used on forwarders in Britain are of Swedish or Finnish manufacture.

Because of their larger load carrying capacity, the cost of the actual movement of timber is less per cubic metre for forwarders than for other tractors. This affects requirements for forest roads, as forwarders can extract economically over long distances and so roads can be spaced further apart. This aspect is discussed in Chapter 13 'Forest roads'.

The ability to carry timber economically over fairly long distances, entirely on wheels, makes forwarders particularly attractive for work on estate woodlands. They can travel over intervening fields with minimum damage to grass and the amount of stacking space required at roadside is little because the crane can make high stacks. Timber extracted by forwarder is generally clean.

Effective use of forwarders requires careful planning and control of preparatory work. Extraction routes should be carefully laid out and crops thinned or felled to concentrate produce for quick and easy loading. Unless there are minor products with the very high values which will cover the high costs of extracting a relatively small volume of each product it is generally desirable to cut timber for forwarder extraction to only two, or occasionally three, specifications. Furthermore, timber is cut to specification before it is extracted and a buffer stock of material ready for extraction is usually necessary to ensure good machine utilisation. This requires close liaison with customers to ensure balance of supply and demand by end-product specifications.

As a general rule forwarder output should be machine capacity per hour in use, e.g. a 10 tonne forwarder should average 10 m^3 per hour or better.

Skidders

These are tractors which extract by lifting one end of the load clear of the ground and pulling it out with the other end dragging on the ground. Timber pieces, poles or whole trees can be extracted in this way. Skidders can be of several types:

1. Two-wheel drive farm tractors with engines of around 50 bhp, fitted with safety cab and extra guarding on sump, radiator and wheel valves, and with some form of butt plate at the rear. Load attachment can be by a small rear-mounted winch, single or double-drum, or by a simple hydraulic grapple.
2. Larger farm/industrial tractors with engines in the range of 60 to 80 bhp; nearly always with 4-wheel drive, and safety cab, extra guarding and butt plate. Usually equipped with a double-drum 3 or 4-tonne winch, and often with a front-mounted stacking blade as well.
3. Specifically designed forest tractors with frame steering, and engine sizes generally from 80 bhp to 150 bhp and above. They have all the features of type 2, and can have winches of up to 10 tonne pull. They are also available with rear-mounted hydraulic grapples as an alternative to the winch.

Because a skidder suspends its load behind the rear wheels, weight distribution is important. Most farm tractors carry a greater proportion of weight on their rear wheels in the unladen state, and when used as skidders are grossly unbalanced. All type 1 skidders require front weight to correct this. Type 2 skidders also require front ballast, though the front stacking blade may assist. The frame-steered skidders, in contrast, start with a front-rear wheel ratio of 60:40, which becomes a near-ideal 50:50 when the load is attached.

Rough forest terrain requires good ground clearance. Farm tractors, particularly the smaller ones, may have only 300 mm clearance, which limits their use on rough ground. The best of the type 2 skidders have about 450 mm, which is generally adequate; frame-steered skidders normally have 470–500 mm or more.

The size of the skidder required is largely determined by the average load size. A rough guide is that 30 flywheel bhp are required for each cubic metre of load. This rule holds good up to 120 bhp or so; above this size, horsepower requirements are somewhat less, perhaps 20–25 bhp per cubic metre.

Small agricultural tractors can be highly manoeuvrable with a turning radius of about 3.0 m. Many of the type 2 skidders can achieve 6.0 m turning radius, but in both cases brakes have to be used to 'skid steer'. Frame-steered skidders generally have smaller turning radii than conventional tractors of equivalent size, and do not require to use brakes for tight turns. In rough, boulder-strewn conditions the frame-steered skidders are far superior, because of more precise steering and better axle oscillation. In soft ground, the performance of types 1 and 2 can be improved by the use of demountable band tracks ('half tracks'), but conventional front-wheel steering becomes progressively less effective as conditions deteriorate.

Specially-designed wheel chains will greatly improve tractor performance in rough and moderately soft conditions. On the poorest bearing surfaces, large flotation tyres are a help, together with the use of branches and tops to form a 'mat' over which the machines can run.

Table 12.1 Classification of terrain

Class				
1	*2*	*3*	*4*	*5*
Ground conditions				
Very good	*Good*	*Average*	*Poor*	*Very poor*
e.g. dry sands and gravels	Firm mineral soils	Soft mineral or ironpan soils in drier areas	Peaty gleys in drier areas; soft mineral soils in wetter areas	Peaty gleys in wetter areas; deep peats
Ground roughness				
Very even	*Slightly uneven*	*Uneven*	*Rough*	*Very rough*
e.g. obstacles (boulders, plough furrows, etc.) small or widely spaced	Intermediate	Obstacles of 40 cm at 1.5–5 m spacing	Intermediate	Obstacles of 60 cm or more at 1.5–5 m
Slope				
Level	*Gentle*	*Moderate*	*Steep*	*Very steep*
0–10%	10–20%	20–33%	33–50%	50%+
0–6°	6–11°	11–18°	18–27°	27°+

Sites are described by the class numbers. A 4.3.2 site means:

    4. Poor ground conditions.

    3. Uneven ground.

    2. Gentle slope.

The standard order of 'Ground conditions, Ground roughness, Slope,' must always be observed. The examples of ground conditions and ground roughness given above are to illustrate typical instances, and are not intended as precise definitions of the classes.

Grapple skidders are available but most skidders in general use are used with detachable sliding choker hooks, to which poles are fastened by detachable slings, called chokers. Chain chokers are common, but polypropylene rope chokers are better, being cheaper and lighter. A single winch rope (9 mm diameter is typical for work in smaller conifers) can carry six choker hooks comfortably, which allows perhaps 10 or 12 small poles to be attached. At, say, 0.07 m³ per pole, this is not a full load. So double-drum winches should always be chosen for small timber work, thus allowing twice the number of chokers to be used. Only in this way can economic load sizes be obtained. Double-drum winches are better than single-drum for average tree sizes of up to 0.5 m³. Above this size, single-drum winches can be used efficiently.

Three- or four-tonne winches are adequate for the general run of conifer and small hardwood logging. Larger winches may be necessary for large hardwoods, or where it is particularly desirable to have drums with the capacity to carry a long rope. Modern tractor extraction uses the winch as a means of load assembly only; it relies on getting the tractor as near the timber as possible, then pulling it out by tractor power, not by winching, but the load can be dropped in more difficult terrain and then winched into the skidder once the obstruction has been cleared. This technique cannot be used with grapple skidders because there is no facility to retrieve the load. Earlier techniques using a tractor as a means of transporting and powering a massive single-drum winch, which then moved the timber from stump to roadside by winching only, are now rarely employed, having been supplanted by more efficient skidders.

Crawler tractors were formerly used as skidders but their use in this country is now confined to a few larger timber operations. High cost of track maintenance and inability to run on public roads are major disadvantages.

Cablecranes

These are ropeway systems where timber is extracted by means of moving cables, powered by a stationary winch. The timber load is usually carried wholly or partially clear of the ground. Two types of cablecrane are in general use:

1. *High lead cablecranes*. These are double-drum winches, generally mounted on a tractor. One drum hauls in the 'main-line' with load attached, the other pulls in the 'haul-back' line, which passes round a pulley block on a spar tree at the far end of the cableway and so to the main line, drawing it out again. A 6 or 7 m tower mounted on the tractor, and the height of the 'tail block' on the spar tree, help to raise the cables and load off the ground. The lifting effect is increased by suspending the load from a block, running on the haul-back line: each winch drum has a clutch and brake, and by applying the haul-back drum brake when the haul-in drum pulls in the load, the line system tightens and lifts the load. Loads can be picked up 10–12 m or more from the line of the cablecrane.

2. *Skyline cablecranes*. These also have two main rope drums but the load is supported by a block running on a tensioned fixed cable, the 'skyline'. This burden cable may be held by fixed supports at intervals along its length.

Cablecranes used in this country are those based on the Norwegian Igland double-drum winches, or the 'Timbermaster' models manufactured by G & R Smith, Aberfeldy. The former can be tractor or trailer-mounted, while the Timbermaster is now only trailer-mounted. Skylines require additional drums to carry the skyline cable and a light cable, the 'straw-line', which the riggers lay out first of all and which is then used to pull out the heavier ropes.

High lead cablecranes are the more efficient over short distances, up to 120 m maximum extraction distance, depending on site. Distances beyond this become difficult to extract by high lead, and 180 m represents the limit for this type of machine. Skyline cablecranes can operate at ranges of up to 600 m with equipment on the lines described above. Ranges greater than this are possible with special cablecranes of Norwegian or Austrian manufacture, but there are few instances where extraction distance is so great as to require their use.

In almost every case it is preferable to use skidders or forwarders for extraction if at all possible owing to the high cost of extraction using cablecranes. Cablecranes need a crew of at least two men and their outputs are generally well below efficient tractor operations. Cablecranes can, though, extract timber on the most difficult sites where all other methods fail.

Loaders

Timber handling, stacking and loading by hand, is extremely hard work and should be replaced by mechanical handling wherever possible. The maximum size of billet for manual handling should not exceed 30 kg. The main types of loader are:

1. *Hydraulic 'knuckleboom' loaders.* These can be lorry-mounted or tractor-mounted and their use on forwarders is described above. Lorry-mounted loaders are usually mounted behind the cab, though mid-body or tail mounting are sometimes used. A demountable lorry crane is also obtainable, so that the crane is left behind in the forest and the lorry can carry its full payload, undiminished by weight of the crane. Knuckleboom loaders are available in a wide range of sizes, with maximum reaches of 4 m to 14 m, and lifting torque of from 2 to 10 tonne-metres or more. Loaders with a reach of 5–6 m lifting torque of 3 tonne-metres are commonest in this country at present.

2. *Front-mounted loaders.* These are purpose-built, high-capacity loaders, which are very efficient if there is a sufficiently high volume to keep them fully employed. Maximum lift height is about 3.8 m, and lifting capacity is in the range of 4 to 7 tonnes as a rule.

3. *Tractor foreloaders.* Basically farm tractors with foreloader attachments. These are machines which make timber handling possible at low cost. Maximum lifting capacity is about one tonne.

The tractor foreloaders are the cheapest but are limited to relatively simple operations, front-mounted loaders are the most efficient but require high-volume operation. Both these types need a certain amount of space to move around. The knuckleboom loaders are the most versatile and most used. The choice of loader depends on type of produce handled and frequency of use.

Harvesting systems

Tree-length system

In the past, most of the timber cut in Britain was harvested by this system. The tree is felled and delimbed at stump; extracted by tractor or cable-crane to roadside; crosscut into sawlogs and other products (pulpwood, stakes, etc.), and these products are then sorted and stacked for collection by lorries.

The principal variation of this system is when the sawlog part of the stem is cut off at stump and extracted separately from the rest of the stem. This is usually done to make sorting at roadside easier, so that sawlogs can be stacked separately from other products. However, the shorter pieces may reduce the load size, and so the efficiency, of the extraction. This variation is common in hardwood logging where the main stem may be extracted entire and branches made into short cordwood pieces at stump.

Tree-length harvesting needs careful supervision to ensure that the three phases of felling, extraction and crosscutting are kept in step with each other. It allows a number of different products to be cut from the stems and sorted at roadside. The concentration of crosscutting means that this can be done by a skilled operator, trained to select the cutting points that will give maximum value of products cut. This is particularly important with valuable timber.

Although forwarders can extract in this system if the poles are not too long, skidders are normally used. Cablecranes can also carry out tree-length extraction, though roadside space for crosscutting is necessary.

Shortwood system

Here the feller combines delimbing with crosscutting at stump, so that all subsequent extraction handles only saleable products and all waste is left in the forest. This system can be highly efficient if a smaller number of products are cut. More than four products presents difficulties of sorting, both at stump and roadside.

Shortwood is relatively easy to organise and control, with only two phases of felling/delimbing/crosscutting and extraction to keep in balance, but poor organisation can be very costly – either by underutilised extraction equipment or weight loss from excessive stocks at stump.

Winch skidders are unsuitable for shortwood work; either the chokering of many short pieces is too time-consuming, or the preparation of large enough piles of billets (perhaps with pre-set wire slings) requires too much work by fellers. Grapple skidders can extract billets but the short pieces mean inefficiently small loads. Forwarders are the ideal extraction method for shortwood, exactly suited to the bulk-handling concept of this system. Cable-cranes can also operate shortwood efficiently, and the elimination of roadside crosscutting makes the system particularly suitable for mountain forests where roadside space is limited or non-existent.

Other systems

There is currently a rapid switch to mechanised harvesting and this trend is likely to continue in the future. Recent technical developments have produced efficient and reliable processors (machines which delimb and crosscut trees to the required products) and harvesters (machines with processor functions plus the ability to fell standing trees). These machines can be used for clear felling and for thinning, presenting shortwood products in the stand similar to manual shortwood working.

There are a number of possible harvesting systems incorporating the process of chipping. The whole tree can be chipped, or only part of the stem and branches, and the chipping can be done at stump,

rack, roadside or depot. Chip systems have not yet been developed as harvesting systems to any extent in this country.

Choice of system

Shortwood has an important advantage in small-size crops, i.e. where average tree cut is 0.1 m³ or less. The small trees are cut into logs or billets at an early stage and thereafter the timber is handled not as small trees but large bundles. Tree-length work retains the tree as the unit of load until a late stage. This is less efficient with small stems but can be advantageous with large trees. The main advantages and disadvantages of the two systems are summarised below in Table 12.2.

Table 12.2   Comparison of harvesting systems

Shortwood system	Tree-length system
Efficient with small and large trees.	Less efficient on trees smaller than 0.1 m³ average.
Two-phase system, easier to supervise.	Three-phase system needs good co-ordination.
Preferably not more than three products.	Several products can be cut. Working space necessary at roadside.
Stacking space only required at roadside. (Can be loaded direct on to transport.)	Sorting and stacking required at roadside. (This can be mechanised.)
Fellers pile smaller billets in wood.	Timber dirty in wet conditions.
Lower density of roads required for forwarder extraction.	Higher density of roads required to organise skidder extraction.

Harvesting techniques

Felling
Organisation

The underlying principle is that felling should facilitate later operations, particularly extraction. If no rack system exists the racks should be marked out to suit the particular extraction system. An existing rack system should be checked and improved if necessary. Racks required for particular extraction methods are described later.

The felling area should be divided into sections. Each section is felled by one, or at most two, fellers.

It is essential to keep a safe working distance between fellers. This should be not less than twice the height of the tallest tree to be cut. If possible the felling sections should be sufficiently uniform to allow a single piecework price to be set for the whole section.

Felling should be carried out in an orderly manner, following organised felling methods to give the best possible presentation for extraction, as the extraction rate is the key factor in harvesting organisation. Felling should follow established techniques, making maximum use of aid tools and with the fellers carrying out minimum movement of the timber.

Bed processor working on clear felling.

Modern working methods reduce effort and increase output. In bench felling, trees are first felled at right angles to the general felling direction to provide supports across which trees are subsequently felled. The resultant increased working height greatly facilitates snedding, and movement of poles or large end-products is eased by their pivoting at points of balance on the bench. With contour felling, benches are aligned up and downhill and gravity assists with produce movement to timber zones.

FELLING LARGE HARDWOODS

Very large open grown or overmature hardwood trees should not be felled using normal forestry techniques. These trees are difficult and dangerous to fell and timber quality may be ruined due to splits or other breakages caused by inappropriate felling methods. It is essential that the operator looks out for dead wood and insecure branches both in the trees to be felled, and in adjacent crowns. It is essential to maintain constant awareness of likely danger during the felling operation and especially when the tree begins to fall.

When the tree is felled removal of branches can be very dangerous and the operator must continually watch for the tree rolling or for springback when cutting branches. Heavy branches should be gradually reduced in length rather than cut off at the stem.

As with all harvesting operations the felling of large hardwood trees should never be undertaken without adequate training and supervision.

Training is essential.

This concentration of produce speeds up forwarder or cablecrane extraction. Contour felling has the added advantage of increased safety on steep ground where conventional strip felling may give very unstable snedding, crosscutting and stacking conditions.

Extraction with forwarders
Organisation
Racks must be planned and marked beforehand. They should be straight, up and downhill if possible, avoiding side slopes. Minimum width is 1.25 m plus forwarder width, and wider on bends, soft or rough terrain. Rack spacing should be 20–30 m in thinnings, 15 m or less on clear felling. Spacing should be such that all produce can be reached by the knuckleboom loader of the forwarder.

Extraction with skidders
Organisation
The extraction routes, or 'racks', must be planned and clearly marked on the ground before felling starts. The selection of routes should not be left to fellers or tractor drivers. The best direction is generally straight up and downhill, with as few bends as possible. In thinnings, racks should be at least 1.0–1.25 m wider than the maximum width of the tractors, and preferably wider on soft or rocky ground. Spacing should be close enough for the felled trees to be easily accessible from the rack; 25 m centre-to-centre spacing is common in thinning, and on clear felling this can be reduced to 15 m. Racks should be curved at junctions and main road exits to avoid damage by the load to standing trees. Stretches of firm, even ground should be utilised for main racks, which are cut wider than normal, and on which fast driving is possible.

Tip-first extraction gives higher outputs than butt-first when winch skidders are used, particularly with small trees. Fellers should leave 2 cm branch projections on the last whorl, to give a good grip for the choker slings. Butt-first extraction is easier for grapple-skidders and is often desirable with larger stems because the butt log suffers less damage, particularly in rocky terrain. On steeper, firm ground, butt-first extraction may give better traction than tip-first.

Extraction with cablecranes
Organisation
The choice of high lead or skyline cablecrane depends on the road system at the forest. If the existing road system is dense, at 270–300 m spacing or less, high-lead cablecranes will be the more economic. If road spacing is wider, up to 900 m, skylines should be chosen. If the forest area is unroaded, the road network should be laid out for cablecranes with a maximum range of 500 m.

Good planning of the extraction racks is more important for cablecranes than for any other means of extraction. In mountain forests when this method is used, stacking space on roadsides is usually limited and this often determines the position of racks in thinning operations. Clear fellings usually allow more effective use of available stacking space. Stacking on sloping ground requires care in building up a secure base for the stack. 'Offset' working allows stacking on the road carriageway but this blocks the road.

As well as starting as an acceptable stacking space, racks should:

- be straight – this is essential;
- be 3.0–3.5 m wide;
- be spaced at 20–27 m;
- have adequate spar and anchor trees; and
- if possible, be parallel, all the same length, at right angles to the road.

If possible, avoid convex slopes for high lead rack alignment. Racks for skylines can be laid out on convex slopes, particularly where knolls, etc., provide higher points on which intermediate supports can be erected. In both cases racks on side slopes should be avoided.

The best solution to the problem of restricted stacking space is regular clearance of produce by lorries. Other solutions rely on moving the produce from the rack mouth to an adjacent or distant stacking site by trailers, forwarders, hydratong-grapple skidders, etc., or by special rigging techniques which allow the cablecrane to move timber laterally along the road.

Roadside and depot conversion
Shortwood harvesting requires only stacking space at roadside, which makes it well suited to cablecrane extraction on narrow mountain roads. All tree-length extraction requires greater stacking space. Occasionally the timber can be delivered to the customer in long lengths but in most cases conversion must be done in the forest.

Roadside crosscutting and processing (i.e. peeling, splitting, ripping, pointing stakes, etc.) is a form of depot working where the work is spread out in a linear fashion. With adequate road width it is possible to accommodate the full range of conversion operations, but it is normal to find considerable interference between operations causing delays. This can often be accepted and there are no hard and fast rules as to when roadside conversion (giving shorter extraction distances but greater conversion difficulties) should be replaced by conversion depots (with longer extraction distances but more efficient conversion). Whichever is chosen, the principles of efficient working are the same.

Harvesting machine nomenclature

Tree definitions

Tree length or pole length – a felled tree, in its length to the cut-off top diameter, with the branches removed.

Whole tree – a felled tree, with all its branches and top intact.

Shortwood – the individual product lengths crosscut from a delimbed pole.

Line skidder

A tractor, normally 4-wheeled, fitted with one or two winches carrying up to 70 metres of wire rope (the 'line') to which the felled trees/poles are attached. The winches are powered either mechanically from the power take off or hydraulically. The load is winched in to the tractor, butt or tip first, and extracted with one end trailing on the ground.

Grapple skidder

A similar tractor but with a hydraulically operated grapple mounted at the rear instead of winches. Loads are extracted part suspended, normally with the butts in the grapple. This system does not allow the operator to drop the load and then retrieve it as can be done with line skidders in difficult terrain. Unloading at the processing point is instantaneous on opening the grapple.

Clam-bunk skidder

A high output 4, 6 or 8-wheeled purpose-built machine with an inverted grapple on the carrying base and a knuckleboom loader for loading individual poles/trees. The load is held in the hydraulically operated grapple and extracted partially suspended. Unloading is instantaneous when the grapple jaws are opened at the processing point. The knuckleboom loader can be used for tidying or restacking if necessary.

Forwarder

A trailer system where shortwood is carried fully suspended on the trailer and loaded by means of a knuckleboom loader.

Tractor/trailer forwarder

A 4-wheeled or tracked tractor with a towed trailer and with a knuckleboom loader mounted on the tractor or on the trailer. The terrain capability of such units is limited to the terrain capability of the tractor.

Purpose-built forwarder

A specially designed unit with an integral trailer or bunk for carrying shortwood. Available in 4, 6 or 8-wheeled configuration/drive and with articulated frame steering. The loaders are normally mounted to the rear of the articulation point, but can also be mounted over the roof on the front part of the machine. 4-wheeled units normally have equal sized wheels, 6-wheeled with larger diameter front wheels, and 8-wheeled units with equal sized wheels. 8-wheeled units normally exert a lower ground pressure and show advantages on very soft ground, especially when fitted with wide section flotation tyres.

Grapple saw

Generally a forwarder base machine, but can be any stable independent machine with a knuckleboom loader, fitted with a specially modified grapple incorporating a hydraulically driven chain saw. The chain saw is built as an integral part of the grapple, mounted to one side of the grapple jaws. It can be used for cross cutting individual poles, or a grapple bundle of poles, at roadside landing or in the wood. Can only be used effectively for products with a wide tolerance as there is only visual estimate of length.

Felling head

The felling mechanism, normally hydraulically operated, used for mechanised felling. The head clamps on to the butt of a standing tree before severing the stem from the butt. Cutting may be carried out by hydraulically powered chain saw or shear.

Feller buncher

A purpose-built machine capable of felling individual trees, holding them in a vertical position, and placing them on the ground in bunches. Some machines have the facility to accumulate 3–5 smaller trees before placing them on the ground. The felling head may be mounted on the end of a boom, and work within the reach of the boom, or with the head close coupled to the base machine, when it is necessary for the machine to approach every tree.

Feller skidder

A felling/extracting machine with a boom mounted felling head which fells the tree and loads it by the butt on to the carrying unit. As with the clam-bunk skidder the whole trees are extracted to a processing point.

Delimber

A machine, also known as a limber, designed to remove the branches from a felled tree, leaving a trimmed out pole. Few delimbers are currently manufactured having been overtaken by processors and harvesters. Most processors can be operated as delimbers if necessary.

Processor

Multifunctional machines, also known as limber-buckers, which remove the branches, cross cut to shortwood and cut off the top of the felled tree. There are three main types of processor in operation, as listed below.

Bed processor

A machine normally based on a modified (shortened) forwarder chassis, with the processor bed mounted on the rear section in place of the bunk. The rotatable processor bed consists of a feed system provided with feed rollers, spiked wheels or tyred wheels, which pull the trees through the delimbing knives. The knives, which are mounted on the infeed side, normally comprise a fixed bottom knife and two moving, hydraulically pressurised, wrap around knives which carry out the delimbing. A hydraulically operated chain saw on the outlet side, operated manually or automatically, cross cuts to the required product length. In addition there is a hydraulically operated shear blade for topping the tree.

Grapple processor

A similar base unit machine to the bed processor, but with a compact processor mounted on the end of a loader boom, with a similar processing function. Claimed advantages of grapple processors are higher output levels and better timber presentation because the processing takes place near ground level, and the boom mounted processor can be moved to any desired position. Large capacity loaders are generally required to operate grapple processors.

Sliding boom processor

This type of processor operates on a different principle in that the tree is pulled through the knives on a push/pull principle. The boom acts as a grapple for picking up the butt of a felled tree and the knives on the telescopic boom carry out the delimbing while the butt end is held in the grapple. Repositioning of the grapple occurs as processing progresses along the tree. An advantage of this mode of operation is that there is no slippage in the feed system as can occur with feed rollers.

Harvester (bed processor base)

A processor with the additional function of felling as well as processing, also known as a feller-limber-bucker. Harvesters are normally heavier and more powerful than processors, and are fitted with high capacity knuckleboom loaders capable of dealing with trees up to about 1 m^3. Felling is carried out by a compact boom mounted felling head which does not need to support the tree in a vertical position. As the tree is severed, it is pulled towards the harvester, and the butt placed in the processor bed for the same processing operation as described for the bed processor. Stump treatment systems can be fitted to felling heads.

Tree length harvester

A harvester which fells the tree and only carries out the delimbing function without cross-cutting the tree into products. Trimmed poles are deposited on the ground either singly or in bundles when the harvester has a facility to accumulate poles. The trimmed poles can be extracted in the pole length or converted by motor manual methods to shortwood *in situ*.

Grapple harvester

A harvesting head is a compact felling, delimbing and cross-cutting device which is hydraulically operated and is usually mounted on either a purpose built wheeled or an excavator base. Diameter sensing and length regulation are available and a stump treatment system can be fitted. The grapple harvester has advantages in cost and flexibility of application over the bed processor based harvester.

13　Forest roads

The function of forest roads is to provide access for the transport of timber to the market and also for general management purposes. Roads are essential in all but the smallest woods, but they are costly to construct. It is important that they should be planned and designed with care.

Forest road planning

Forest road construction involves significant capital expenditure and continuing charges for road maintenance; but a good road system will reduce the amount of cross-country movement of timber in extraction operations, and may allow greater use of larger, more economical road transport vehicles for delivery to the customer. The purpose of planning roads for timber exploitation is to try to achieve the combination of road cost and extraction cost (and sometimes road haulage cost as well) which gives the lowest overall cost of moving timber. There may, of course, be other purposes for roads through woodlands, such as general management, access for sporting and to property beyond the forest edge. Such needs may generally be accommodated within the road system designed for.timber extraction.

An investigation of road planning calculations, taking into account a substantial number of cases involving different terrain conditions, with variable factors of road construction and timber movement costs, has resulted in a general assumption that the optimum spacing for well-constructed roads in large forests is about 1000 metres. This wide spacing arises from the major developments in efficient high capacity extraction machines, such as skidders and, especially, forwarders. A detailed calculation of the best road spacing can be made for any given wood. In smaller woods, densities of 20 or more metres per hectare may well be appropriate.

Public highways

The internal forest road system should be planned with the public highway layout in mind: the public roads to which connection is to be made must be of a standard sufficient to carry the traffic generated by the forest. All new accesses, and major alterations to existing accesses, on to the public highway system require approval by the Local Highway Authority. An approach should be made to the Highway Department in the first instance to ensure that the proposals being made are in accordance with the regulations. When the plans have been approved by the Local Highway Authority it will be necessary to ensure that they are constructed in accordance with their specification.

The effect of terrain, soils and other factors on road location

Road location is greatly affected by topography and ground conditions, both of which vary over a wide range in Britain. The normal procedure on cross-sloping ground is to locate the road alignment in such a way that excavation is minimised, but the

179

C.D. MacMahon, former Head of Engineering Division

Table 13.1   Summary of forest road standards

Item	Feature	Dimension		Remarks
Tree felling for forest road	Clearance width	Variable		Depends on site conditions but must accommodate all roadworks and associated drainage, with adequate clearance to avoid excessive shading of road.
Road formation	Formation width	min 4.7 m		Batters – upper as steep as possible. Lower batters normally 1 in 1¼.
Road formation	Formation width on peat	min 5.6 m		Road formation is constructed on top of deep peat but with shallow peat up to 500 mm the peat can be excavated.
Road formation	Formation camber	min 75 mm		On slack gradients road camber is increased to 90 mm.
Road formation	Crossfall	min 150 mm but not exceeding 190 mm		On roads located on steep cross slopes crossfall replaces camber.
Gradient	Longitudinal	max 10%		Except on horizontal curves where road pavement width has to be increased.
Gradient	Longitudinal	min 1%		On flat country for efficient drainage.
Road pavement	Width	3.2 m		Standard width but increased for sharp horizontal curves as necessary.
Forest road	Horizontal curves	Radius	Road pavement width	Road pavement is widened on sharp horizontal curves for vehicles up to 32 ton (articulated) and up to 28 ton (fixed platform). Road pavement widening is achieved on the inside of the curve with a straight transition, 15 m length, to the inner radius.
		m	m	
		60.0	3.2	
		45.0	3.5	
		30.0	4.0	
		25.0	4.2	
		20.0	4.5	
		15.0	5.0	

Table 13.1 Summary of forest road standards *(continued)*

Item	Feature	Dimension	Remarks
Forest road pavement	Thickness of (i) base course + surfacing course (ii) combined base and surfacing course	Varies from 150 mm to more than 450 mm	Dry bound macadam construction.
Turning places	Width Length	4 m 21 m	Set out in the form of a T.
Passing places	Width Length	4 m 33 m	

terrain may well introduce the problems of both horizontal and vertical curvature. It is essential to avoid substantial outcrops of rock, but excavation is less of a difficulty where the rock can be ripped using a large angle dozer fitted with a hydraulically operated ripper. Forming roads on deep peat, in embankment form, is commonly practised especially when morainic, or other suitable deposits occur nearby as sources of good construction material. In high rainfall areas the existence of streams and rivers poses a special problem of road location, and it is not uncommon for a bridge or culvert crossing to dictate the position of the future road.

Harvesting systems, whether involving forwarder, skidder or cablecrane methods of timber extraction, as well as engineering design considerations, influence road location and alignment. Consideration of the incidence, size and positions of timber handling, stacking and conversion facilities, is also important.

Forest road standards

In the United Kingdom the Road Vehicles (Construction and Use) Regulations 1986 permit the use of vehicles of up to 30.49 tonnes gross vehicle weight of the 4-axled rigid type and up to 38 tonnes gross vehicle weight of the 5-axled articulated type. Both these types of vehicles can have a maximum overall width of 2.5 metres. The maximum permitted length of a rigid vehicle is 12 metres and the Road Vehicles (Construction and Use) (Amendment) Regulations 1990 increased the maximum permitted length of an articulated vehicle to 16.5 metres. Maximum axle loads are 10.17 tonnes and 10.5 tonnes respectively. A vehicle/trailer combination is permitted to have a maximum gross vehicle weight of 24.39 tonnes (if certain conditions are fulfilled they can go up to 32.52 tonnes). A maximum axle load of 10.5 tonnes and a maximum overall length of 18 metres.

Because of the distance from the forest to the

market, it is normally good economic practice to use the largest vehicle available and the summary of forest road standards set out in Table 13.1 is designed for this purpose. However, there may be a case for lower standard roads suitable for use by vehicles less than maximum size in small plantations, especially if existing forest roads and/or the existing approach public highway are sub-standard and material has to be hauled to a local mill.

Survey methods

Once the location of the road in terms of a broad corridor has been planned, the road survey can take place. If the ground conditions are difficult, and especially if bridges or large culverts are concerned, then a detailed survey will no doubt be warranted. This will involve the preparation of a longitudinal section, with cross-sections, and a plan. These provide the basis for detailed design of the road, taking into account such aspects as the specification data, water crossings, soil conditions, road construction methods, the type of plant to be used on construction, the availability of suitable material and other items.

Construction of roads

In private woodlands it is more than probable that most road construction work will be put out to contract. This involves the preparation of contract documents even if only in a simple form. The main items of the road specification recorded elsewhere in this chapter should be observed, in relation to the particular site, to achieve a forest road of efficient and sound design. It is not feasible to describe all the types of ground conditions here, but one of the most common is that of a cross-slope in firm sub-soils.

Road construction in these conditions takes the form of a shelf, excavated by a large angle dozer (normally fitted with hydraulically operated ripper), or medium sized excavator with back hoe equipment. The latter is used mainly where the ground tends to be wet and sleeper mats may have to be considered. Where hard conditions prevail, a rock ripper can often be applied to facilitate rock excavation, and this is of great benefit compared with the operations of drilling and blasting of rock, which tend to be fairly slow, much more costly and less safe.

Another type of ground condition which is quite common in the uplands occurs where peaty soils prevail, on fairly flat ground, and this includes both shallow and deep peat. Where the peat is shallow it is usually excavated, and the sub-grade thus exposed is shaped accordingly. Where deep peat is concerned the established method is to construct a road embankment on top of the peat using suitable, locally won, materials.

The importance of an efficient drainage system for the road, in the form of side drains, lateral water crossings and road camber or cross-fall, cannot be over-emphasised. It is imperative for bridges and culverts to have waterway areas of adequate size and to be constructed of sound materials.

The road formations resulting from the various types of construction are compacted, so far as possible, using a vibratory roller. In wet and soft conditions the compaction of road formation is often difficult to achieve.

The next consideration is that of pavement construction. Materials from proved sources, such as existing quarries, can be used but on many sites considerations of cost make it necessary to search for and identify materials such as gravels, morainic deposits, burnt shale, tunnel spoil, etc., for use in road works. The plant required for the construction of the road pavement consists basically of the front loading shovel working at the rock or gravel face or stockpile. Tipper lorries then transport the material to roadhead, where it is spread on the road formation by a small angle dozer or similar equipment. However, where this is not available, spreading by hand is feasible. The pavement should be capable of being maintained by motor grader and compacted by roller. If the latter equipment is not available, compaction by traffic may have to suffice.

The major influence on road performance is the drainage of the surface layers. It is important, even for low grade roads, and for any form of construction, to have a camber on the road sufficient to dissipate rainfall quickly and to ensure that the surface is compacted and as dense as possible to prevent rain water entering the road and causing potholes. The road surface should be well clear of standing water and the side drains should be made in a manner that will ensure quick runoff. Typical cross-sections of the road are shown in Figure 13.1.

Road construction and maintenance plant

In view of the references to the type of construction plant used on roadworks it is useful to set this down in tabulated form. The schedule shown in Table 13.2 provides an indication of the types of machine and their recommended application.

Bridge design, construction and maintenance

The incidence of water-crossings which are encountered in forest road alignments is a feature of many forests. Normally the need is for permanent bridges, designed with adequate waterway area, and capable of taking Department of Transport's Standard Highway loadings, which covers the largest vehicle permitted under the Construction and Use Regulations. Both reinforced concrete and mass concrete abut-

Table 13.2　Machinery for road construction

Type of machine/equipment	Recommended application
Crawler tractor/angle dozer	Light angle dozing work and spreading stone on road formation.
Large crawler tractor/angle dozer (over 100 dbhp)	Excavate and side casting, road formations in cross, sloping ground. In addition, cutting and filling longitudinally on an undulating road alignment.
Large crawler tractor/angle dozer (over 100 dbhp) fitted with ripper	Ripping of rock in quarries and on road alignments.
Tracked excavator fitted with back hoe ($\frac{1}{2}$–$\frac{3}{4}$ m^3 bucket capacity)	Excavation of road formation in soft ground – using sleeper mats if necessary.
Front loading shovel (approx. 1 m^3 bucket capacity)	Loading of stone at quarry.
Digger/loader	Excavation of drains, culverting. Loading stone on minor works.
Compressors, tractor-mounted or towed (with rock drilling equipment)	Drilling in rock.
Tractor and trailer	Transporting stones from source to roadhead on minor work.
Dumper/dump waggon	Transporting stone from source to roadhead over short distances.
Medium to large tipping lorry	Transporting stone from source to roadhead on major work.
Motor grader	Maintenance of roads.
Vibrating roller	Compaction of road stone.

ments are suitable, although shortage of skilled labour would suggest that the latter design is more appropriate in small forest blocks.

As far as the deck superstructure is concerned the design, for spans up to 6.0 m, is that of a simply supported reinforced concrete slab. Precast, prestressed concrete inverted tee beams, with *in situ* concrete infill and topping, acting compositely, and with mild steel distribution, are used for superstructure spans over 6.0 m and below 15 m. This type of design is both economical and calls for little skilled labour in erection. A different type of superstructure for spans in excess of 15 m is advocated, in the form of steel Universal Beams acting compositely with an *in situ* reinforced concrete slab.

If there is a need for a temporary bridge a Baily bridge of required span would satisfy the need. This type of bridge was designed for military use, is expensive to maintain, and should be used only as a temporary expedient. It is possible to design short span bridges in timber.

It is usual in private forestry work for bridge design to be carried out by a consultant and the bridge constructed under contract, following the usual civil engineering procedure.

A number of forest blocks on private estates have old, existing road bridges. Experience has taught that some of these are unsafe for timber vehicles. It is essential that the existing bridges should be examined in detail, by a qualified engineer, and their load capacities assessed. Restriction notices should be erected, and reconstruction or replacement of the sub-standard bridge may be required. Load carrying assessment of existing bridges should initially be calculated in accordance with the Department of Transport's *The assessment of highway bridges and structures*. If any limits thus calculated are too restrictive then the effects of specific vehicles only should be considered.

Maintenance of roads

Generally, roads in small forest blocks tend to be used only intermittently, and consequently do not suffer the deterioration that is experienced by the main traffic route through a large block of woodland. Forest roads should be designed with mechanised maintenance in mind, and where there are a lot of small blocks, it is feasible for a motor grader team to move from block to block on a pre-arranged system, reinstating the road as required. This work may be necessary only at intervals of a few years. Where plant cannot be justified, the repair of the road surface can be done by hand on the road, using a tractor with tipping trailer or tipping lorry to supply the material from the source used for maintenance purposes. If compaction equipment is unavailable, compaction by traffic may be the answer, although not the ideal one. The reinstatement of the road surface is important but another essential item is that of regular maintenance of roadside drains and culverts, including the clearance of debris and silt. Among the other features is the need to maintain roadside bank batters at a safe angle and generally to clear brash and timber waste from the vicinity of the road. A forest road, especially in a small block, may be used not only for vehicle passage but also as a platform for the working of timber. This throws an added burden on road maintenance.

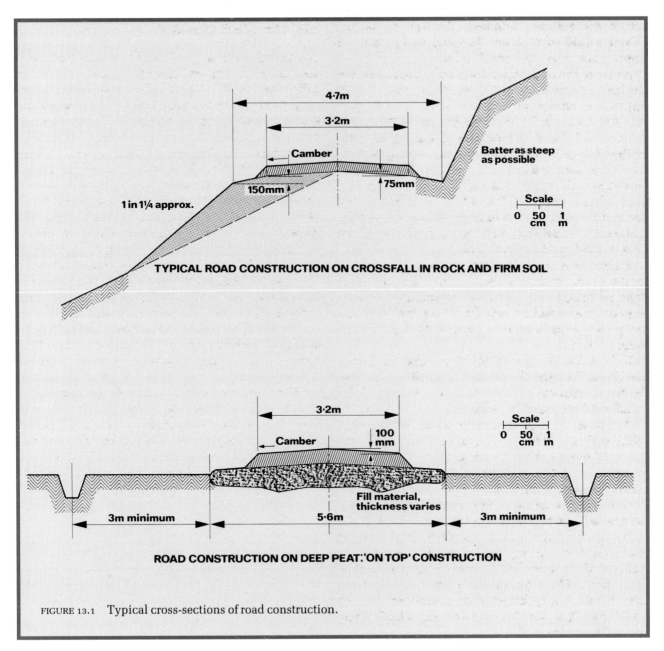

4·7m

3·2m

Camber

Batter as steep
as possible

150mm

75mm

1 in 1¼ approx.

Scale

0   50   1
     cm   m

TYPICAL ROAD CONSTRUCTION ON CROSSFALL IN ROCK AND FIRM SOIL

3·2m

Camber

**100
mm**

Scale

0   50   1
     cm   m

Fill material,
thickness varies

3m minimum

5·6m

3m minimum

ROAD CONSTRUCTION ON DEEP PEAT:'ON TOP' CONSTRUCTION

FIGURE 13.1   Typical cross-sections of road construction.

14   Marketing and utilisation

Good marketing requires sound knowledge of what is to be sold and what the timber is worth. The first requirement means that a grower should have:

1. A long-term estimate of production from the woodland covering the next 10–20 years; such an estimate, even in broad terms, indicates the size of the marketing task in the years ahead and allows the prospects for co-operative marketing to be assessed.

2. A short-term estimate for production for each of the next 5 years. The estimates for the next 2 years should be in greater detail and should give information on the planned cut by species, size, class and whether thinning, clear felling or selective cutting in mature stands. However, market conditions may change and plans should be sufficiently flexible to allow for this.

Knowledge of timber value requires a study of local, regional and national markets both of price levels and current demand. Such knowledge is important even where trees are sold standing, as the price the buyer can afford to pay is determined by the markets he can supply. The Timber Growers' organisation (TGUK) can provide their members with extensive market information and can advise on merchants and contractors for harvesting and haulage, etc. Forestry consultants in practically every part of the country can prepare production estimates, measure and value timber and provide marketing and general management advice.

COUNTY LISTS OF MILLS, MERCHANTS AND CONTRACTORS

The Forestry Commission's publication *Marketing for small woodlands* is published for counties in England and Wales to assist individuals who have timber to sell and those who act in an advisory capacity to woodland owners, to get in touch with those who seek to buy timber. These lists will not in themselves sell timber and they do not provide any guide to prices because these are variable and depend on market conditions.

The lists have been structured to highlight the information that buyers will normally want to know:

1. The tree species, dimension of timber to be sold – sawlogs, pulpwood, etc.

2. The approximate quantity. A full lorryload is about 20 m³.

3. Where is the timber to be sold? Standing, felled (at stump or at roadside)?

4. Is haulage required, or can the timber be delivered?

Owners are advised to seek professional advice if in doubt about marketing their timber.

D.A. Greig and **D.A. Thompson**, Harvesting and Marketing Division

Licensing of felling

The felling of growing trees is controlled by a licensing system under the Forestry Act 1967. There are exceptions to the need for a licence, the main examples being:

1. The felling is in accordance with an approved plan of operations under one of the Forestry Commission's grant schemes.
2. The trees are in a garden, orchard, churchyard or public open space.
3. The trees are all below 8 cm in diameter measured 1.3 m from the ground or in the case of thinnings below 10 cm in diameter or in the case of coppice or underwood below 15 cm in diameter.
4. The trees are interfering with permitted development or statutory works by public bodies.
5. The trees are dead, dangerous, causing a nuisance or are badly affected by Dutch elm disease.
6. The felling is in compliance with an Act of Parliament.

As the licensing system applies only to the felling of growing trees, no licence is necessary to cut up trees that have blown over even if a whole wood has blown down. Most other fellings must first be licensed by the Forestry Commission, and the appropriate regional conservator (see addresses in the Appendix) will supply the necessary application form on request. Any owner who foresees problems in completing it is invited to seek the Conservator's advice when requesting the form.

Licences often bear conditions requiring the land to be replanted after felling but the owner is always consulted before such conditions are imposed and should he object to the proposed conditions he would be advised of the appeal procedure. Information on the control of tree felling is contained in the

Forestry Commission's *Grants and procedures* booklet.

Except where trees are covered by a Tree Preservation Order, forestry work is not subject to control under the Town and Country Planning Acts. Nevertheless, as the felling of trees can conspicuously change the appearance of the countryside, the Forestry Commission consults local planning and other interested authorities about most applications for licences, particularly where the trees are in an area of high amenity value.

SITES OF SPECIAL SCIENTIFIC INTEREST

Section 28 of the Wildlife and Countryside Act 1981 requires English Nature, Scottish Natural Heritage and the Countryside Council for Wales to notify owners and occupiers of land within an SSSI of any operations that appear likely to cause damage to scientific interest. It also requires owners and occupiers intending to undertake such operations to give the appropriate national authority for nature conservation in England, Scotland or Wales notice in writing of their intentions so that it may assess the likely effect on the scientific interest. Where felling operations are involved, notification must be given to the nature conservation authority whether or not an application is to be made to the Forestry Commission for a felling licence.

Methods of sale

This section discusses the marketing arrangements that may be used to sell trees or their products to best advantage.

Home-grown softwood
timbers used in
construction.

Home-grown softwood timbers used in construction.

Negotiation

Here the prices and other conditions of sale are agreed between buyer and seller, and a suitable contract drawn up between them. Some growers negotiate mutually advantageous sales with the same merchant for several years in succession, and this has the benefit of stabilising the merchant's labour force, including sub-contractors, who are often extensively employed by merchants. It also allows the merchant to invest in harvesting equipment, with greater assurance. Negotiated sales depend on the grower having a particularly good knowledge of timber value, including the merchant's probable markets and revenue, his costs and the amount he can be expected to be able to pay for the timber in

consequence. If the grower does not possess this knowledge, the services of a consultant or one of the growers' organisations are necessary.

Tender

Sales by tender are competitive and can generally be expected to give a true reflection of market prices. They can be invited from selected merchants or by advertising in the trade press. The precise terms of sale must be determined before advertising, and copies sent to interested potential buyers so that they know exactly what these conditions are before tendering. This is necessary because acceptance of a tender automatically concludes a contract on the advertised or published conditions.

Auction

Auction sales avoid the drawback of the tendering system, whereby a merchant can lose a parcel of timber because his tender is only marginally lower than the highest offer received and he has no chance to revise his price. Such an outcome could disrupt the merchant's working, resulting in possible inefficiency and lower prices being offered. Auctions also attract more interest and this can bring better prices.

It is possible that major buyers will outbid smaller competitors at auctions, and this may not be to the grower's long-term benefit. One can only sell specific goods ('ascertained goods') at auction, and some types of produce may be difficult to describe with the accuracy an auction sale legally demands. Sawlogs arising from future felling, where the range of sizes may be difficult to estimate, are an example. On a falling market, merchants tend not to bid at auctions and this can accelerate the fall in prices.

Auction sale expenses make it uneconomic to sell isolated timber parcels in this way. The Forestry Commission holds regular auction sales in various parts of the country, and private growers can make arrangements to sell lots immediately after the auction of Forestry Commission lots, so reducing sale costs.

No one method of sale is best for all circumstances, and even the most experienced growers will find it advantageous to consult the growers' organisation. This is particularly true of competitive sales, where careful timing and grouping of advertisements and advance warning of future sales is necessary to achieve maximum effect. There are also advantages to be gained by co-ordinating marketing efforts with neighbouring growers, so as to be able to offer larger and more concentrated volumes of timber in a locality. This enables growers, or merchants buying standing timber, to make the best use of harvesting resources, to negotiate better road haulage contracts, and be in a stronger selling position with regard to customers.

Point of sale

Timber can be sold standing, as felled trees in the length or as converted produce: the relative merits are discussed below.

Standing sales

The sale of trees 'standing' to a timber merchant is simple, involving the grower in the least outlay, work and commercial risk. It also tells him, before a tree is cut, what his financial return will be. The trees to be sold are either individually marked or the boundaries of the area to be worked are marked and the individual trees to be felled within that area are indicated in some way.

It may be preferable to divide a large parcel of timber into two or more smaller lots, especially if the timber comprises widely different types, such as small conifer thinnings and mature hardwoods. Each parcel should be described separately, giving estimated number of trees, estimated total volume, and estimated average volume per tree for each species. Recording the number of trees by breast height diameter classes, and calculating the total volume estimated for each class, is often helpful to both sides in arriving at the price to be paid. Owners whose local supervisors are not skilled in estimating volumes of standing trees, should seek the services of a forestry consultant or their growers' organisation.

The conditions under which the timber is to be sold should be clearly defined, so that the growers' interests are safeguarded and contingencies catered for. Unnecessary restrictions will reduce the price a buyer is prepared to offer, and should be avoided. Conditions of sale should be notified to interested merchants before they inspect the timber.

Standing sale contracts

When a sale bargain has been made, the conditions of sale should be incorporated in a legally binding contract signed by both parties. It is not possible to list every detail which might be covered by an individual contract, but the following items are normally included:

1. A general description of the timber included in the sale. A precise description of the boundaries of stands, of the methods used to identify trees to be cut, and details of estimated numbers of trees and volumes, should all be given. Method and time of measurement (e.g. before or after felling) should be specified. Many growers find it preferable to sell a stated or estimated number of trees, rather than a volume of timber since the number of trees is easier to assess than the number of cubic metres they contain. In addition, in the event of any dispute over the quantities involved

in a sale, it is comparatively simple to verify the number of trees cut, by counting stumps: verifying the volume of trees after removal is much more uncertain. It is, of course, up to the buyer to satisfy himself that the estimate of volume stated, but not guaranteed, in the sale particulars, is sufficiently accurate.

2. The purchase price, method of payment (either by lump sum or per cubic metre or per tonne), terms of payment, the method of invoicing, and the point at which ownership passes from grower to the purchaser.

    Growers should note that sales by volume can either be by measured volume or by weight converted to volume using an agreed volume–weight conversion factor. This latter method, like sale by weight on a price-per-tonne basis, is easy to operate using the weight tickets of the delivery lorries as a control and is sensible provided the grower is satisfied that all timber has been weighed. Sales by weight operate in favour of the grower if the material is despatched promptly and weighed in a green state, but against the grower and the road haulier if the produce loses weight by drying-out.

3. The period of the contract, date of entry by the purchaser, completion date for the whole contract, and the dates for removal of produce and purchaser's equipment.

    Provided the starting dates are sufficiently far ahead to allow the buyer enough time to organise his harvesting operations, markets, etc., it is as well for the grower to insist that the completion dates agreed with the buyer be adhered to. Extensions to completion dates should be exceptional. If the completion date is uncertain at the time the sale is agreed, the contract might specify the circumstances under which extension would be granted, the maximum length of extension and the extra sums payable by the buyer in consideration of such extension. Time limits for removal of produce even if already paid for, should also be adhered to firmly. Merchants should not be allowed to use the forest as free storage space.

4. Method of working. The standard of workmanship required, e.g. height of stumps, disposal of lop and top, avoidance of damage to remaining trees, drains, ditches and streams, fences and walls, and extraction routes. Special requirements regarding spar, support and anchor trees necessary for cablecrane work, and the removal of processing waste such as sawdust, peelings, etc., from processing sites. Any logging methods not acceptable to the purchaser should be specified, e.g. use of crawler tractors or skidders on forest roads.

5. Access routes to be used including their ownership and condition of their use preferably supported by a map.

6. Working sites. An indication of sites owned by the seller which may be used by the purchaser, and under what conditions, e.g. sites for processing, stacking, seasoning, loading, erection of sawmills and other buildings. Any provisos regarding entry on seller's land let to tenants.

7. Liability. The settlement of third party claims for damages caused by the purchaser or his employees, and claims for damages to the seller's property, including standing trees not in the sale. Claims by the purchaser for improvements carried out by him. Descriptions of the condition of seller's properties, e.g. fences, gates, roads, buildings, etc., will be required to facilitate subsequent settlement of claims, and such descriptions must be agreed by the purchaser.

8. Responsibility for safety under the Health and Safety at Work Act 1974.

9. Fire precautions. The precautions to be observed by the 'purchaser or his employees, including liability of the latter to assist in extinguishing fires.

10. The treatment of stumps after felling.

11. The restrictions on use of, or keeping of animals on the forest or estate by the purchaser or his employees.

12. The limitations on employment of sub-contractors by the purchaser and the obligations by sub-contractors to observe general conditions of sale.

13. Force majeure.

14. Action in the event of serious fire or windthrow.

15. Breaches of contract giving the right to terminate.

16. Action on termination of the contract.

Felled trees in the length

Some growers may not wish to sell their timber standing, for various reasons. For instance some of the timber may be required for conversion in the grower's own sawmill, it may be desirable to do the felling at a particular season or the owner may want to provide work for woodsmen in the worst months of winter. Sometimes trees for sale may be too scattered to attract a timber merchant, or may have to be felled with extreme' care to avoid damage to remaining young or specially valuable trees.

Whole trees can be sold felled at stump or at rideside or roadside. A purchaser should be found before the trees are felled, and the sale should be subject to a contract covering the same points as for a standing sale.

Sale of converted produce

Where the felled trees are to be converted and sold as separate products, e.g. sawlogs, pulpwood, mining timber, etc., it is essential to find a purchaser for the produce before a tree is felled. It is also essential to have trained men and the right equipment available. Above all, the supervisor in charge of the operations must be competent and experienced.

Sales of produce can be made through or to a timber merchant, who will often be willing to arrange collection and transport by road haulage vehicles. Other customers may require produce to be delivered, either on the grower's transport or through a road haulage firm. The latter is generally preferable, as road haulage is a specialised business. In negotiating or quoting prices, it should be made clear whether prices are 'at roadside', where the customer does his own haulage and loading; 'free on transport' (FOT), where the grower is responsible for loading the customer's vehicles; or 'delivered', where the grower is responsible for loading and delivery.

Contracts for the sale of converted produce are simpler than those for standing sales but the essential points on duration of the agreement, description of the produce, quantity, property at risk, measurement, price and method of payment should be covered.

Prices

Because home produced timber accounts for only a small part of the country's total needs, the prices of imported timber and wood-based products have a strong influence on the general level of home timber prices. Large timber users, such as the major pulpwood and chipboard makers, negotiate contract prices with their suppliers, which reflect the price of the imported finished product, haulage distance to mill, species supplied, etc. Sawlogs and standing trees are usually sold to timber merchants whose prices may be affected by their particular requirements. If a merchant has a full order book and his round timber stocks are low, he may be prepared to pay higher than normal prices: conversely, if trade is slack and a merchant's stocks are high, he is likely to consider only low prices for further purchases.

Timber quality affects price to a varying degree, according to the locality and markets. For example, high quality Douglas fir may command a good price if local millers can themselves obtain premium prices from their customers, but may fetch no more than average prices if the local users are interested only in general purpose timber. The factors which also affect price are tree size, species, size of parcel, ease of harvesting and access by road haulage vehicles. These, together with local or regional demand, will have to be taken into account when deciding the market value of a parcel of timber. Each factor will carry varying weight in different circumstances.

It must be emphasised that the grower who sells only occasional lots is in a weak selling position. It is not uncommon to find parcels worth thousands of pounds being sold with no independent valuation. Professional advice is available, and its use is strongly recommended.

The Forestry Commission regularly publishes average prices paid for standing sales of conifers from its forests and indices showing changes in log and standing sale prices. These schedules appear in forestry journals and the trade press as do the prices realised at Forestry Commission auctions.

Products

The market for particular products may vary considerably in different parts of the country, and from time to time, and the grower is strongly recommended to find out what markets are currently available before preparing specific products. The following paragraphs are a guide to the main categories of round timber produce in Great Britain.

Conifer sawlogs

British sawn softwoods compete with imported timber in the major sawn timber markets, although very little British grown softwood is suitable for high grade joinery work. There is a trend in the imported trade to reduce the range of specifications readily available and this results in there generally being a good market for British sawn softwood in the less common size categories. British sawmillers have the advantage of being able to respond rapidly to a requirement for special sizes, although this may result in the sawlog specification being changed at short notice. All logs over 14 cm top diameter overbark can be regarded as potential sawlog material. Certain sawmills which use chipper headrigs can prepare squared timber from a round log, converting the outside rounded portions to saleable chips and these sawmills can take logs of top diameters of less than 14 cm. The sawlog specifications normally used by the Forestry Commission are given in the Commission's Field Book 9 *Classification and presentation of softwood sawlogs.*

Hardwood sawlogs

Prices for hardwood sawlogs vary according to species, quality and diameter to a much greater degree than those for conifer sawlogs. The highest prices are paid for veneer logs, a considerable proportion of which are exported for slicing or peeling in Europe. Logs which are not quite good enough for veneer may make joinery grade timber, while logs of poorer grade are normally converted to fencing material or mining timber. Because of the degree of price varia-

Wood-based panel products. *Clockwise from top:* wood chipboard, oriented strand board, medium density fibreboard, wood wool cement slab, cement bonded particleboard, hardboard (a fibre building board).

tion and specialisation in certain sectors of the market, it is particularly important that owners of good quality hardwood parcels seek professional advice on the optimum timing and method of sale.

Industrial roundwood

Pulp mills and particleboard mills in Great Britain require small diameter material normally termed small roundwood. Small roundwood billets for these markets are usually supplied in lengths between 1 m and 3 m with a diameter range between 2.5 cm and 40 cm. It is important to obtain details of specifications and prices direct from the firms concerned. Methods of payment, e.g. by weight or volume, and delivery arrangements must also be agreed with the firm in advance.

The purely softwood pulp mills at Shotton in north Wales, at Workington and at Caledonian Paper's new mill at Irvine require spruce almost exclusively. The pulp mill at Sudbrook in Gwent accepts almost any hardwood species.

Wood-based panel board mills are located near Inverness; at Cowey near Stirling and Irvine, Ayrshire; at Hexham, Northumberland; South Molton, Devon; and at Chirk in Wales. They will accept most coniferous species and certain manufacturers may also accept hardwoods. Most board mills produce chipboard and a large proportion of their wood requirement is provided in the form of sawmill residues. The oriented strandboard plant near Inverness produces a board made from wafers of wood. One of the plants at Cowey produces a medium density fibreboard.

Fencing materials

Sizes and specifications of fencing materials vary considerably (Table 14.1). Oak, sweet chestnut and larch are commonly used without preservation treatment, where they contain a high proportion of durable heartwood. Other species are generally preserved, with pressure treatment the most effective process. Fencing materials are made to a very wide range of specifications (see Table 14.1) and producers are advised to check BS 1722 for specific requirements.

Telegraph poles

British Telecom purchase a proportion of their annual pole requirements from British growers. Pines, larch and Douglas fir are currently accepted but the poles must be of a high quality and have to be inspected and passed in the forest by British Telecom pole inspectors. The full specifications are given in BS 1990.

Table 14.1 Fencing timber specifications

Type	Material specification
Post and rail fences for roadsides, morticed, cattle-proof	Posts, sawn: 150 × 75 mm, 2.1 m long Rails, sawn: 90 × 40 mm, 2.7 m long Intermediate posts: 90 × 40 mm, 1.8 m long
Motorway fences	Posts, sawn: 150 × 75 mm or 130 × 100 mm minimum, 2.3 m long Rails: 90 × 40 mm (hardwood) or 100 × 40 mm (softwood) All species to be pressure treated with preservative
Post and rail fences nailed	Posts, sawn: 140 × 65 mm, 2.0 m long Rails: 90 × 40 mm

Post and wire fences	Posts, sawn: 75 × 75 mm, 1.7 m long or 90 × 90 mm, 1.7 m long
	   or quartered from 180–200 mm top diameter or round, 75–90 mm top diameter or half-round, 100 mm face at top
	Straining posts, sawn: 150 × 150 mm or 180 × 180 mm
	   or round, 180–200 mm top diameter,
	   all 2.1–2.3 m length

Deer fences	Posts: 75 × 75 mm, 2.6 m long, or equivalent in quartered material Straining posts: 230 mm top diameter, 3.2 m length

Turnery poles

Some turneries take hardwood, notably birch, ash, sycamore, beech, and common alder normally in poles of 7.5 cm minimum and 18 cm maximum top diameter, in lengths of 2.0 m and upwards. Turnery squares, sawn from round logs, are also used in a variety of hardwoods.

Rustic poles

This can be a useful market near towns, for conifers (especially larch) and sometimes hardwoods. Sizes range from 2.5 to 6.0 m length, with top diameter of 2 cm and butts of 4–10 cm.

Other forest produce

Over five million Christmas trees are sold in Britain each year and they can be a profitable market although quality is becoming increasingly important. The British Christmas Tree Growers' Association was formed in 1980 to advise on the management of Christmas tree plantations and provide marketing information.

Foliage of western red cedar, silver firs, Lawson cypress and holly are sold to the florist trade for wreaths and decoration, but the market is largely fragmented and uncoordinated.

15 Landscape design

Forestry has had one of the greatest impacts on rural landscapes in Britain this century and it is therefore important to find a balance between the economic demands of forestry and the requirements of the landscape. More resources will often need to be allocated in sensitive areas such as National Parks, Environmentally Sensitive Areas, National Scenic Areas in Scotland, Areas of Outstanding Natural Beauty and Areas of Great Landscape Value where landscapes are of higher quality. In most cases careful landscape design will be needed to achieve a satisfactory appearance for the forest, with cost as the balancing factor.

Design principles

Of the numerous aesthetic factors which affect forest design, shapes related to landform, scale and diversity are fundamental and objective principles for the achievement of a satisfactory appearance.

SHAPE is of paramount importance, especially that of external boundaries and felling coupes. These edges have the most visual impact due to the combined effect of tree heights and their shadows and colour contrast. In both cases they should be irregular, diagonal to the contour and reflect the shape of the ground by rising uphill in hollows and falling downhill on convex slopes. The extent of these inflexions should increase with the size and prominence of the hollow or convexity. Visually intrusive geometric effects should be avoided and in particular:

- long straight edges
- right angles
- parallel edges
- symmetrical shapes
- vertical boundaries (perpendicular to contours)
- horizontal boundaries (following contour).

Appropriate shapes for external margins, species and coupe boundaries should be developed as follows:

D. Campbell and **S. Bell**, Environment Branch

- imitating shapes from the surrounding landscape, e.g. the angular geology of the Lake District or the smooth flowing shapes of Northumberland and the Borders.
- following visual forces in landform (see 'Shape' above).
- following natural vegetation shapes (although fussy scale and conflict with landform forces should be avoided).

SCALE depends on the amount of landscape that is seen. It increases with the vertical height, breadth of view and distance to the observer. With a number of viewpoints scale often needs to be gradually changed from one part of the landscape to another; usually larger at hill top and decreasing towards the valley floor.

DIVERSITY depends on the number of different features within the landscape. The apparent uniformity of the forest should be reduced by revealing open space, views, crags, rocks, water and scrub, and creating felling coupes and a varied age structure. A diversity of tree species including broadleaves should be developed.

Design method and techniques

While contour, soil and stock maps, aerial photographs and crop information are needed for planning, accurate sketches are essential for design. These should be based on a photograph or tracing from a projected transparency. Besides information on crop details the following factors should be recorded on a contour map and/or sketch as a basis for design:

- hollow and convex slopes (represented by upward and downward arrows)

- existing intrusive design
- features to provide diversity
- areas suitable for larch and broadleaves
- existing and potential recreation facilities
- potential deer control areas.

All the information should then be analysed to identify problems, opportunities and priorities. Design should be carried out on the main sketched view, in the following order, then checked and adjusted from subsidiary views:

1. Complete set of felling coupes (at restocking).
2. Timing of felling coupes (at restocking).
3. Design and improvements of external boundaries.
4. Species layout.

If extensive improvement to the external boundary is needed at restocking it may need to be carried out before the felling design.

Planting design

The following points should be considered when implementing design principles for planting:

- A satisfactory external forest margin should be achieved before species layout begins.
- Side margins should be tapered diagonally towards the lower edge and can be successfully terminated at major watercourses.
- Leave unplanted those areas that would screen main landscape features.
- Vary the width of unplanted verges beside public roads.
- A geometric lower edge is acceptable where there is a strong pattern of field enclosures, with irregular groups of broadleaved trees along the lower edge and extending up major watercourses.
- Avoid thin slivers of open ground or forest in long views or near skylines.

- Include areas of larch where possible to provide diversity; preferably located on convexities to highlight landform.
- Avoid belts by shaping their general alignment, varying their width, and leaving irregular gaps where possible. (Irregular groups and areas of broadleaved trees extending up watercourses are preferred.)

Felling design

Clear felling and restocking provide important opportunities for improving the appearance of the forest by the correction of previous bad design and introducing greater variety of open space (felling coupes) and tree size (Figure 15.1). The development of a well-designed pattern of successive felling coupes and a varied age structure is essential to such an increase in visual diversity. The appearance of restocking is so dependent on the shape and timing of felling coupes that they must be designed together.

The following points are important when implementing design principles:

- Where short views are important the apparent scale of large coupes can be reduced by adopting a very irregular shape or by retaining areas in the foreground to be felled when restocking behind is established.
- The apparent scale of coupes can be increased in the long view by extending felling to include the forest edge.
- A calculated risk of windthrow may need to be taken to achieve a satisfactory design. Wherever possible coupe boundaries should follow windfirm edges that are sympathetically shaped to landform. Intrusive windfirm shapes should be avoided.

- Skylines should either appear completely open or as solid forest; diffuse belts and scattered trees appear out of scale and should be avoided.
- With cablecrane systems currently working to 650 m from roadside there is little need to leave intrusive belts of trees at the upper margin. Where this is unavoidable the belt should be broken into groups by felling.
- The practice of screening coupes with belts of trees is intrusive and to be avoided. Well placed groups of trees will reduce the impact of lop and top and give a more sympathetic landscape composition.
- Where there is a need to retain single trees in felling areas only well formed individuals in coherent groups should be kept.

Replanting design

Replanting layout should include any improvements to external margins. The screening of open spaces, views, crags, water, broadleaved trees and other features should be avoided by leaving land unplanted.

Species layout should follow the same design principles and coincide with coupe boundaries as closely as possible.

Advice

Limited general advice on forest landscape design is available from local Forestry Commission staff. More detailed and comprehensive advice can be obtained, e.g. for sensitive areas, from a landscape architect or suitably qualified members of the Institute of Chartered Foresters. Names of landscape and forestry consultants can be obtained respectively from the Landscape Institute, 6/7 Barnard Mews, London SW11 1QU or from the Institute of Chartered Foresters, 22 Walker Street, Edinburgh EH3 7HR.

Landscape design training

There are several further education establishments that provide both graduate and post-graduate training in landscape design at degree equivalent status (refer to Landscape Institute for details).

The Forestry Training Council, in association with the Forestry Commission, offers a short course, specifically dealing with forest design, for private woodland owners and managers.

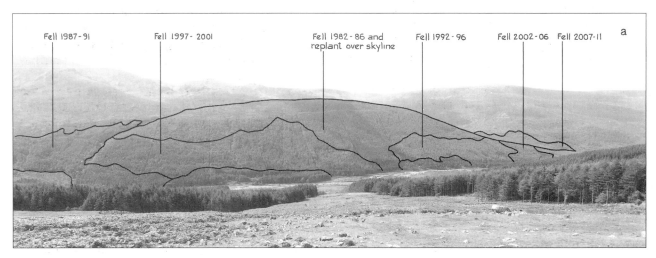

FIGURE 15.1 Felling and replanting design for part of Ennerdale Forest (Cumbria): (a) pattern of coupes and approximate felling dates, (b) proposed species pattern and improvements to external boundaries and landscape.

16   Recreation in the forest

The structure of society is changing and leisure opportunities are increasing. Whilst many people are spending more of their leisure time in the countryside others, reliant upon public transport, are unable to do so. All this plays a significant part in influencing the needs of different people for appropriate recreation opportunities and facilities, which recreation providers need to identify. The ability of the forest to absorb large numbers of people engaged in a wide range of recreational activities, without detriment to the landscape, is now widely appreciated by visitors and planners alike especially in respect of woodlands close to towns and holiday centres.

Since the opening of the first National Forest Park in 1935, the Forestry Commission has allowed public access for the quiet enjoyment of its forests, wherever it is able to do so. Its policy now is to satisfy the needs of as wide a range of the community as possible by providing appropriate recreation facilities of a high standard of design. The provision of recreation opportunities for the visitor is an important consideration for private forestry as well. Under the Woodland Grant Scheme as in previous schemes applicants must be prepared to enter into discussions with the Forestry Commission and local authorities in relation to access and recreation.

Recreational values and uses

The main recreational value of forests and woodlands is that they offer a unique setting of trees in great variety, wildlife, sheltered spaces, quietness and fine scenery for the pursuit of a wide range of activities. This can provide different and stimulating experiences and knowledge for our largely urban population, thereby making a significant contribution to the quality of life.

Walking, relaxing and picnicking are by far the most popular activities. Nearer towns they are supplemented by jogging, walking the dog, and informal play by children. These are all satisfied by simple types of recreation provisions, such as car parks and picnic places, which do not require large areas and from whence waymarked walks can encourage visitors to use places and things of interest within the forest.

Leaflets from convenience dispensers as well as discreet signs can interpret the forest, its wildlife and management for the visitor and thus widen the understanding of forestry. In popular areas, the interpretation of the forest and its environment can be augmented usefully by the provision of exhibitions and classroom facilities within a visitor centre building.

The demand for educational visits, cycling and horse riding facilities is often near towns. Forest bridle tracks may have to be created to separate riding from other uses and permits issued at modest charges for its control. Selected forest roads and tracks can also provide attractive opportunities for 'off highway' pedal cycling, which is increasing in popularity. Other well established uses are orienteering, the competitive sport, and wayfaring or forest orienteering, which is the exploration on foot of part of a forest using a map.

D. Campbell and **R.J. Broadhurst**, Environment Branch

Maintaining the quiet of the forest is important; but careful planning can allow limited motor vehicle access along selected forest roads or 'forest drives', for the benefit of people with disabilities, the elderly and families with young children. Provided the forest is large enough and possesses an adequate system of forest roads, the occasional motor sport event can also take place without significant conflict with other uses. It is desirable to organise such events under the auspices of the appropriate national motor sport organisation (see list of useful addresses).

The forest also offers many opportunities for specialist recreational uses, including archery and the traditional field sports of shooting, deer stalking and fishing. These activities can be controlled by let and/or day permit, which can allow their wider availability to the public. The detailed requirements of a wide range of recreation activities can be obtained by reference to appropriate publications in the bibliography. Advice on the encouragement of game birds, wildfowl and small game for sporting in woodlands can be obtained from the Game Conservancy, Fordingbridge, Hampshire.

All of the activities mentioned can be enjoyed by the public over a longer period by the provision of overnight accommodation in the forest. Caravan and tent sites and self-catering forest cabins can be successful enterprises in achieving this aim as well as providing significant returns for their owners.

The impact on the forest

In the planning of recreation schemes, it is essential to identify all the requirements and interactions between different recreation activities, the forest environment and its management. This enables activities to be zoned in the forest, in terms of location, time and level of use so as to minimise possible conflicts. In this way a reasonable balance can be achieved between the provision of recreation and the main production of wood which, usually, is not constrained significantly.

In general, the main influences upon wood production occur in the creation and maintenance of good forest landscapes for recreation. This can include small clearances of trees for vehicle access and for the development of car parks, picnic places, walks, glades and views. The interest of the forest in the vicinity of the facilities may need to be improved by the introduction of a variety of tree species. Broadleaves and larches are especially useful as they provide diversity as well as reducing the fire hazard. Likewise brashing, thinning and sometimes pruning will also be beneficial and will encourage access to the forest. The size and timing of clear felling in certain areas may require adjustment to maintain an interesting landscape or to create variety.

In most situations, the forest has a relatively high carrying capacity and is very robust. However, poor behaviour can cause problems and this is most prevalent in woodlands near towns. In these areas the main problems tend to be vandalism, frequent fires, persistent rubbish dumping, theft of trees and produce, unauthorised access by motor cyclists, disregard for the Country Code, and impediments to some forest operations such as harvesting and pest control at certain times.

All these problems can be solved or mitigated by creative and positive management at reasonable costs. These are detailed in a guide on woodland recreation close to towns *The public in your woods* produced by the Land Decade Educational Council. The increased social benefits obtained from town edge woodlands make the additional management effort worthwhile.

Planning for forest recreation

It is essential to plan recreation projects from the outset in order to achieve a good balance between the needs of the visitor, the objectives of the owner and the potential of the site.

A plan will enable the owner to appraise these issues properly, including costs as well as benefits to himself and the visitor. It should prevent errors arising from development on an *ad hoc* basis, which might require costly remedial treatment at a later stage.

An early consideration is how the owner intends to carry out the planning required to implement a project. He will be influenced by its complexity (e.g. a simple day visitor facility such as car park and walks, as opposed to a campsite or chalet development) and the staff of relevant skills that he has available. In general, it should be possible for an owner to undertake day visitor projects with his own staff, obtaining information/assistance as required from the Forestry Commission and other appropriate bodies such as the local planning authority and national organisations for tourism, sport, recreation and conservation (see list of useful addresses). This approach will be facilitated if a project team, with a designated leader, is appointed to carry out the work throughout all its stages.

If, however, the project is likely to be complex, large and/or located in a sensitive landscape, then it could be worthwhile having the work undertaken by a firm of landscape architects or specialist recreation consultants. The planning authority must, of course, be consulted at an early stage, in order to obtain development approval.

The planning of a recreation project can be divided broadly into survey, analysis, and design, including financial appraisal. Through these three main processes, information about the visitors background and needs, the owners short and long-term objectives (or his 'brief') and the opportunities and limitations of the site, is collected, organised and used creatively to produce an attractive and functional facility at acceptable cost.

Survey

A map at 1:25 000 (2½ inches to the mile) scale or smaller as required, can be helpful in considering the location of possible sites in relation to centres of population, principal traffic routes, main approach roads, other tourist attractions, possible visitor demand, planning considerations, etc.

The local planning authority and regional tourist board should be able to provide guidance on these points as well as for likely demand and marketing. Most trips to the countryside for recreation are made by car within a 50 km (*c.* 30 mile) radius of home. Only a few travel by public transport, while visits to woodland on foot are generally confined to those within 5 km (*c.* 3 miles) of towns.

Sites should be carefully chosen so that they offer the visitor a good quality of environment and enjoyment. It is important that they should accommodate facilities without damage to the visual or natural environment and artefacts of interest. Having selected a particular site a contoured plan, usually at 1:500 scale, is essential at this stage of the survey. All factors affecting the site(s), e.g. main access, public rights of way, existing use, topography, vegetation, and aesthetic quality, should be recorded on one copy of the plan. At the same time the requirements of the owner's brief and any relevant additional information should be noted.

Analysis

All the information collected should then be analysed and organised to provide a basis for design. The assets, defects, problems, opportunities and constraints of the site need to be identified and those most likely to influence the design of the facility recorded on a copy of the plan; this will facilitate the assessment of the interaction of factors. The range of issues to be shown on the analysis plan include: main landscape features, slope in relation to proposed uses, aspect and shelter, important trees/vegetation to be conserved and their stability, estimated areas required for cars, coaches and picnicking, requirements for toilet or other facilities, provision for people with disabilities, possible user conflicts (horse riding, shooting), information signs and proposed walks, viewpoints, etc.

This analysis should indicate the most compatible match between site factors and brief and will enable a zoning plan to be prepared showing the approximate location of various facilities (car park, picnic place, toilets, etc.) and the required vehicle and pedestrian circulation (Figure 16.1). This plan forms the basis for site design.

Principles and practice of recreation design

The importance of providing an enjoyable experience for the visitor has already been stressed. To achieve this it is essential that all recreation sites and associated buildings, structures, and artefacts are designed on sound aesthetic principles.

Principles

In general, a good and well tried approach to woodland recreation is to aim not only for peace and quiet, but for an experience that contrasts significantly with that of the town. Thus in recreation design it is important that the impact of artefacts is reduced to a level where the natural qualities of the site can dominate. Urban materials, light and bright colours should therefore be avoided. The cumulative visual impact of the numerous functional small structures such as traffic barriers, signs, fences, toilets, etc., is often overlooked to the detriment of the facility. While a certain level of diversity is required to prevent boring regimentation, it should be provided by the natural features of the site such as rocks, water, trees, ground vegetation and open space. Careful attention to the detailed and co-ordinated design of these elements is important in maintaining a sense of continuity on the site.

Site design

Site design is developed by applying these principles to the zoning plan produced in the site planning process. The extent and location of all proposed artefacts and retained features (such as roads, car parks, paths, trees, etc.) should be shown on a contoured plan (1:500 scale) with reasonable accuracy. Some details, e.g. a planting design around a car park or building may require to be drawn up at a large scale of 1:200.

Options, costs and benefits

Efficient function and good appearance occasionally coincide in imaginative design but it is often necessary to find a compromise between the two, which may involve additional cost. It is therefore advisable to design a number of options, either on separate plans or by overlays on a single plan, in order to identify that option which is likely to produce the best results at the least or most acceptable cost. Both capital costs and annual running costs need to be considered; to facilitate this it is often convenient to express capital cost as an annual equivalent value. This must be done when comparing options of differing time lengths.

Benefits can accrue to the owner from the direct income obtained by charging for use of the facility, from the management of visitors to avoid conflicts and from good public relations.

Maintenance

The constructed facility should be regularly inspected by management to ensure that a good standard is maintained. Monitoring, by survey, of usage and visitor reaction can often reveal unforeseen problems and/or suggest improvements.

Provision for people with disabilities

Site planning and design should integrate the requirements of people with disabilities whenever possible and provide reasonable opportunities for recreation. This will be mainly for the elderly and those less able to move about, also for the paraplegic, ambulant disabled and where appropriate, the blind.

People with disabilities recognise their limitations but need to feel that they can use the same facilities as others whenever possible. Attention to detail is important. Access to picnic tables, information, the most attractive parts of the site, etc., all need to be considered, as well as parking, toilets and paths. Unnecessary barriers such as steps should be eliminated from any design.

Existing facilities may often be radically improved for the less able through very minor modifications, e.g. a ramp into a building, widening of a toilet cubicle, easing a gradient on a walk (1:40 is ideal), replacement of a stile by a gate, etc.

Those concerned with planning and design should, at an early stage, consult the relevant references listed at the end of this chapter, and national or local access groups and organisations for the disabled.

Main design considerations for car parks, picnic places, woodland/forest walks and small structures

Car parks, picnic places, walks and structures usually form the main components of the type of simple day visitor facility which is in greatest demand and could be provided by a private owner with least intrusion upon his privacy or conflict with the management of his property. For this reason a brief indication of the main design considerations is given here although details will have to be obtained from the relevant further reading references.

Picnic places

Picnic places should be located and oriented for their shelter, aspect (generally SSE-WSW) and view. They are usually close to the car park but with sufficient ground or tree separation to give visual detachment and minimise traffic noise intrusion. A range of picnic furniture from simple benches to picnic tables may well be necessary with more sophisticated structures close to the car park and decreasing provision for visitors penetrating further into the forest. In some situations, no furniture will be needed. At the larger facilities, especially campsites and chalet sites, it may be appropriate to develop children's play areas specifically designed for the countryside.

Access

The sequence of visitor experience from approaching the site, through use of the facilities until departure has a major effect on the enjoyment of the visit. First and last impressions are particularly important. Thus, well before the entrance to the site, landscape improvements may include reshaping the forest edge by felling, thinning, pruning, planting and removal of eyesores, e.g. unnecessary signs, fences or their replacement with improved ones.

Car parks

Typically, a small forest car park should be an informal arrangement of parking spaces in a woodland setting fairly close to a forest edge and serving picnic places and walks. Normally a single access point should be adequate for the car park which should be sufficiently far from the public or forest road to give visual separation; the access road should be curved. The car park should have minimum visual impact on the site and surroundings and yet provide an enjoyable environment for those who wish to stay in their cars. Thus the edges of car parks, roads and paths should be curved on plan and related to underlying land form – rising in concavities and hollows and falling on convexities.

The location of toilets and information points should be clear from the point where the access road enters the car park. Vehicle circulation should be two-way as far as possible to avoid numerous directional signs and allow proper separation of vehicles and pedestrians.

Usually, surfacing will be required and stone aggregates, natural in colour and texture to the locality, should be used. Generally surfaces should not be sealed with tarmac or bitumen except at main accesses and exceptionally heavily trafficked zones. Where sealed surfaces are used they should be top dressed with aggregates of similar local natural colour to that used on other parts of the site.

Natural features should be used wherever possible to limit vehicles to the parking areas. Rock outcrops, sharp changes in ground level, drainage ditches and the tree crop itself are the most appropriate devices. These can be supplemented by artificial barriers appropriate to the site, e.g. short posts amongst trees and low wooden rails or low banks on open areas.

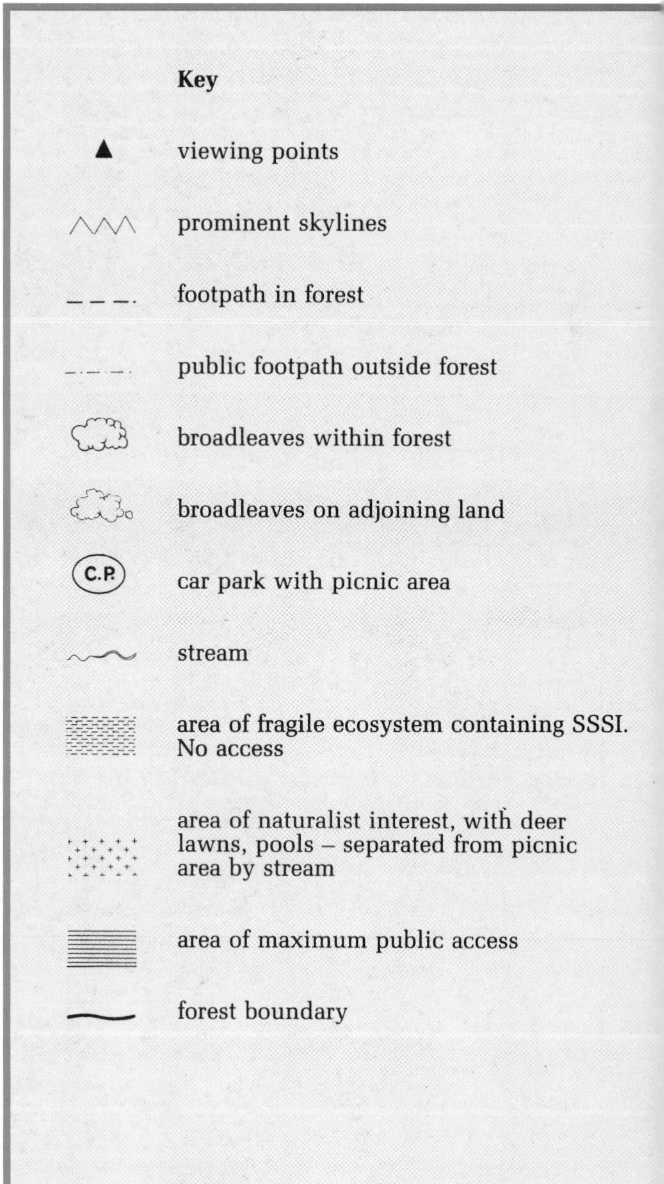

Key

▲	viewing points
∧∧∧	prominent skylines
_ _ _.	footpath in forest
_._ _.	public footpath outside forest
⌂	broadleaves within forest
⌂	broadleaves on adjoining land
(C.P.)	car park with picnic area
∿	stream
▦	area of fragile ecosystem containing SSSI. No access
⋮⋮	area of naturalist interest, with deer lawns, pools – separated from picnic area by stream
≡	area of maximum public access
⌒	forest boundary

FIGURE 16.1   Recreational zoning plan.

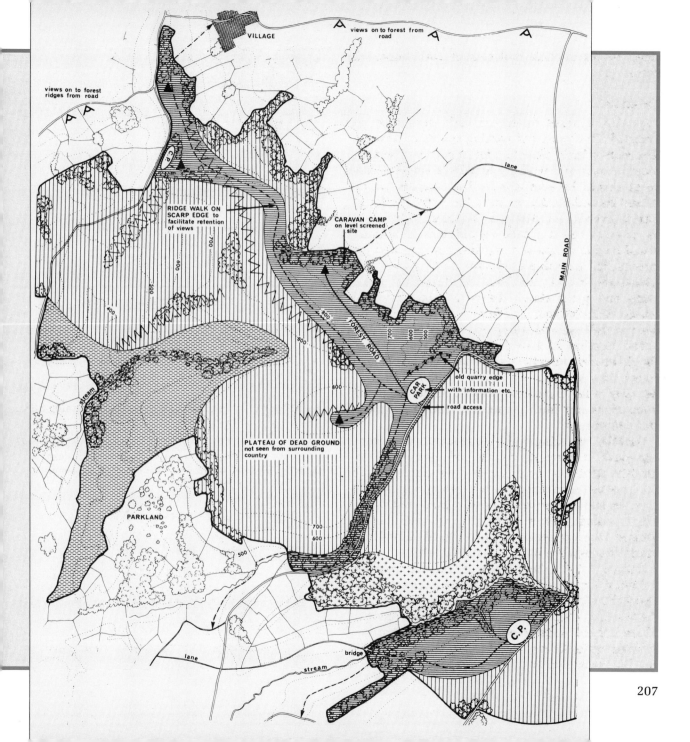

VILLAGE

views on to forest from road

views on to forest ridges from road

RIDGE WALK ON SCARP EDGE to facilitate retention of views

CARAVAN CAMP on level screened site

C.P.

lane

MAIN ROAD

FOREST ROAD

old quarry edge with information etc.

CAR PARK

road access

stream

PLATEAU OF DEAD GROUND not seen from surrounding country

PARKLAND

C.P.

lane

bridge

stream

207

Small buildings and structures

The cumulative visual impact of all the structures required in a recreation facility has a profound effect on its overall appearance. Colour and texture affect the visual impact of all elements. Darker more neutral colours with coarse matt finishes are generally more suited to the rural environment.

Small buildings such as toilets need to be kept as simple as possible. A monopitch roof running with any natural slope and/or with the high wall against a backdrop of trees or rocks is a basic way of providing a building well related to its site.

Generally signs should be of simple design and well constructed and their impact, number and size should be kept to the minimum necessary for satisfactory function. Where a recognised symbol exists it should be used in preference to text.

Forest/woodland walks

The walks should provide for as full a range of physical ability as topography permits. This should range from short gently sloping walks for the less able to a full day's walking in strenuous conditions. The maximum amount of landscape diversity should be included with as much variety, e.g. open spaces of varying width, strong enclosure, long views and short views out of as well as into the wood, different tree sizes and species, moving and still water, and varied vegetation as can be reached by the walk. All should be combined in a well co-ordinated sequence with as much contrast and surprise as possible. The route should be planned to minimise scour and erosion problems and avoid the need for steps. Walkers and horses should not use the same path or track.

Site restoration

Although disturbance to vegetation should be kept to a minimum during construction some bare ground is inevitable at the edges of roads, car parks, etc. It is important to reinstate such areas as soon as possible to maintain a satisfactory appearance on the site. Any harsh geometric edges should be rounded off to develop a smooth, continuous ground plane. Additional tree and shrub planting may also be necessary to improve the setting of buildings, as a screen for cars, to provide separation between picnic benches, etc.

Recreation training

There are a number of further education establishments offering recreation management training at first degree and post graduate level and a large number of short courses – many held at colleges or based in field studies centres and in National parks. The Countryside Commission has produced a useful summary of training opportunities available. The Countryside Council for Wales and Scottish Natural Heritage are well placed to give advice also. Details of some of the shorter courses which may be of particular value to owners and staff involved in recreation are often given in the periodicals serving the recreation and leisure industry.

Financial assistance

Grant aid for recreation schemes is available to the private owner from the three national countryside agencies. Financial assistance may also be available for joint schemes from local authorities and regional Tourist Boards. It may also be possible to obtain sponsorship from the commercial sector for all or part of a recreation scheme.

Table 16.1 Summary of planning and design considerations

Scheme	Objective
1. Prepare a plan 1:2500 scale	Survey the estate and note features of recreational interest.
2. Assess the demand	Consider: population characteristics within day-trip range both for residents and tourists; traffic flow patterns; public transport routes; existing provision of participation levels within a radius of 30 miles; prediction of future trends.
3. Review recreational potential	Compare demand data and the attractiveness of the woodland for recreation. Decide also whether, due to its situation and size, the estate offers a particularly good site for overnight facilities.
4. Prepare a survey plan at 1:500 scale	Record all factors affecting the site; access, rights of way, topography, vegetation, aesthetic quality, owners brief, etc.
5. Prepare an analysis plan at 1:500 scale	Analyse assets, defects, problems, opportunities, constraints, etc., likely to influence the design of the facility.
6. Prepare a zoning plan at 1:500 scale	Show approximate location of car park, picnic place, toilet, walks, etc., as a basis for site design.
7. Prepare a design plan at 1:500 scale with detail at 1:200	Show the extent and precise location of all proposed access points, roads, car parks, paths, vehicle and pedestrian circulation, trees, structure, artefacts, etc., to create a facility, with provision for disabled people, which is pleasant and efficient and which does not intrude on the general landscape. Consider options using overlays or on separate plans.
8. Carry out a financial appraisal	To determine the financial viability and the acceptable level of investment. Assess possibility for grant aid.
9. Submit plans the planning authority	To obtain development permission. Revise plan if necessary (consultation with the planning authority will have started at an early date in the planning process).
10. Progress development	Carefully brief and supervise the construction work. Use the minimum structures consistent with efficiency. The form, materials and location of structures should be chosen with care in harmony with good principles of design. Ensure site is properly restored after reconstruction.
11. Achieve a high standard of maintenance	To ensure visitor satisfaction.
12. Monitor usage and compare with predictions	Adjust management plans if necessary.

Conclusion

Though multiple land use is no stranger to the private estate, in which good integration of different land use objectives is often achieved, there are still few public recreation facilities in private woodlands. There is no doubt that the increasing pressure for recreation in the countryside has brought a real public awareness of the social benefits of the forest. The owner of private woodland is encouraged to welcome the public on his land, and so make a worthwhile contribution towards satisfying the recreational needs of society.

Useful addresses for recreational activities

Auto-Cycle Union
  Millbuck House, Corporation Street, Rugby, Warwickshire CV21 2DN.

British Horse Society
  National Equestrian Centre, Stoneleigh, Kenilworth, Warwickshire CV8 2LR.

British Mountain Bike Federation
  36 Rockingham Road, Kettering, Northants NN6 8HG.

British Orienteering Federation
  Riverdale, Dale Road North, Darley Dale, Matlock, Derbyshire DE4 2JB.

Camping and Caravaning Club
  11 Lower Grosvenor Place, London SW1W 0EY.

Caravan Club
  East Grinstead House, East Grinstead, W. Sussex RH19 1UA.

Centre for Environmental Interpretation
  Manchester Polytechnic, St Augustine's, Lower Chatham Street, Manchester M15 6BY.

Cyclists' Touring Club
  Cotterell House, 69 Meadrow, Godalming, Surrey GU7 7HS.

English Tourist Board
  24 Grosvenor Gardens, London SW1W 0ET.

Game Conservancy
  Burgate Manor, Fordingbridge, Hampshire SP6 1EF.

Institute of Leisure and Amenity Management
  Lower Basildon, Reading, Berks. RG8 9NE.

National Federation of Anglers
  2 Wilson Street, Derby DE1 1PG.

Ramblers' Association
  1/5 Wandsworth Road, London SW8 2LJ.

Royal Association for Disability and Rehabilitation
  25 Mortimer Street, London W1N 8AB.

Royal Automobile Club
  Motor Sports House, Riverside Park, Colnbrook, Slough SL3 0HE.

Scottish Auto-Cycle Union
  'Kippilaw', Longridge Road, Whitburn, West Lothian EH47 0LG.

Scottish Rights of Way Society
  52 Plewlands Gardens, Edinburgh EH10 5JR.

Scottish Sports Council
  Caledonian House, South Gyle, Edinburgh EH12 9DQ

Scottish Tourist Board
  23 Ravelston Terrace, Edinburgh EH4 3EU.

Sports Council
  16 Upper Woburn Place, London WC1H 0QP.

Sports Council for Wales
  Sophia Gardens, Cardiff CF1 9SW.

Wales Tourist Board
  Brunel House, 2 Fitzalen Road, Cardiff CF2 1UY.

17 Planning for the second rotation

The challenge of creating tomorrow's forests from today's plantations is one which is currently facing many forest managers and the debate about how best to achieve this and the type of forest desired is an important one. Substantial areas of upland spruce forests are now reaching the stage where felling of the first generation stands is taking place. Many such forests contain large areas of even-aged plantation planted at a time when attention paid to environmental considerations may have been less than would now be considered appropriate. Felling and restocking provides the opportunity to change what was created 40–50 years ago but if an improvement in forest structure is to be made then felling and restocking must not be a simple reaction to the attainment of economic maturity or the clearance of windthrown stands, or the result will be a perpetuation of the same large even-aged blocks created in the first rotation. What is required is a purposeful management plan which seeks to achieve a business-like timber growing operation within the confines of an environmentally sensitive framework. This chapter describes the principles adopted in formulating such a management plan for Kielder Forest District, as typical of upland spruce forest.

By the early 1980s it had become apparent at Kielder that a long-term view of the desired forest structure was required which would seek to integrate the requirements of efficient operational activities with a planned increase in wildlife and landscape diversity by the imposition of a comprehensive forest management plan. This process has come to be known as restructuring.

OBJECTIVES OF RESTRUCTURING

The aim of restructuring can be stated as a planned means of transition from the present even-aged plantations to a forest structure which provides both a more efficient operational base and an increase in landscape and wildlife diversity. The key elements in the process are:

- identification of landscape zones;
- identification of major watercourses to form the basis of a network of broadleaved woodland corridors;
- planning for the provision of open areas;
- identification of windfirm felling coupe boundaries and the planning of all future coupes;
- planning of the age structure differentials by staggering fellings;
- identification of stands for long-term retention.

Forest zonation

The experience gained in early landscape exercises indicated that Kielder Forest could be divided, on the basis of elevation and topography, into three zones within which differences could be identified with respect to landform, productivity, visibility to the public, species choice, windthrow risk and scope for thinning.

211

R. McIntosh, Forest District Manager, Kielder Forest District

Table 17.1 Changes in management between the first and second rotation under restructuring

Key elements	First rotation	Second rotation
Zones	Zonation limited to corridors alongside major roads and to windthrow hazard classification	Comprehensive zoning on the basis of elevation and topography
Watercourses	No special management	Watercourses form the basis for a network of permanent low density broadleaved woodland corridors
Open areas	No special management	Planned open areas associated with special features or purposes
Compartment boundaries	Mainly grid pattern with little operational value	Permanent windfirm boundaries associated with landform and with operational requirements
Compartment size	Standard size throughout unrelated to landscape, operations or felling plans	Compartment = felling coupe with wide range of sizes linked to the scale of both landscape and operations
Age class	Unplanned and largely even-aged over large areas	Planned diversity with provision for some long-term retention

Lower zone

This zone encompasses the land below 250 m a.s.l. Although only a relatively small part (15%) of the planted area at Kielder, this zone contains the majority of the valley bottom landscapes, the majority of the areas readily visible from public roads and the areas most popular for recreation. The plantations are largely in windthrow hazard classes 3 and 4. This zone contains, therefore, all the stands considered thinnable and is the area of the forest where the constraints of windthrow are least. Furthermore, this zone contains the highest proportion of watercourses, an important factor in determining felling coupe boundaries, and offers, because of the better valley bottom soils, the greatest opportunity for species diversification.

Middle zone

Embracing the land between (approximately) 250 m and 300 m, this zone includes about 37% of the planted area at Kielder. The dominant landform is the typical rounded convexity of the Border hills and much of the forest in this zone presents a middle distance view to travellers on public roads and to visitors. Productivity is generally lower than in the lower zone and, with windthrow hazard classes 4 and 5 predominating, thinning is considered undesirable and windthrow constraints begin to come into play.

Upper zone

All planted land above 300 m at Kielder is contained in this zone which accounts for some 48% of the

Careful planning of felling and restocking in this first generation crop in Devon has led to important improvements in landscape value and in benefits to wildlife.

Table 17.2 Windthrow hazard class at Kielder

Windthrow hazard class	Area (ha)	Terminal height (m)*	Age†
3	770	26	71
4	7 700	23	51
5	17 325	20	47
6	12 705	17	39

* Defined as the top height of the stand when windthrow has affected 40% of the trees.
† The age at which terminal height will be reached in unthinned Sitka spruce stands of general Yield Class 12.

Table 17.3 Planting history of Kielder

Period	Percentage of area planted
1926–30	<1
1931–35	2
1936–40	7
1941–45	6
1946–50	15
1951–55	25
1956–60	12
1961–65	5
1966–70	8
1970–75	10
1976–80	6
1981–85	4

forest. The upper slopes and exposed hill tops are the dominant landform and much of this zone provides a distant view from the main public areas. All stands are in windthrow hazard classes 5 or 6 and there are severe constraints on rotation length. Pro-ductivity is generally lower and this, coupled with the shortened rotations, make it desirable to have larger coupes where harvesting and restocking operations can benefit from economies of scale. Landscape features such as watercourses tend to be smaller and fewer in number in this zone thus making it more difficult to identify windfirm boundaries.

Felling coupes

Felling coupe boundaries

The need to minimise the extension of windthrow into stands adjacent to felled areas, coupled with the need to have distinct, permanent boundaries between coupes (compartments) dictates that coupe boundaries should be at distinct breaks or where breaks are planned in the future with the proviso that this strategy should not create an unacceptable configuration in the landscape. The use of these criteria immediately identifies watercourses and permanent main harvesting roads as the key features. The harvesting road system provides a network of significant breaks throughout the forest which seldom run in completely straight lines either across or up and down slopes and their use as coupe boundaries also ensures that efficient harvesting can take place. Watercourses are frequent throughout the forest and tend to become larger and more concentrated towards the valley bottoms where a wide choice of coupe boundary features is more important. Many of the wider watercourses already provide a distinct break, particularly where the original planting was kept back from the stream edge. As future plans involve either leaving an unplanted zone along watercourses or creating permanent broadleaved woodland, it is envisaged that watercourses which are also natural landscape features will normally provide a windfirm natural break between coupes.

Watercourse management is an essential part of restructuring plantations.

Felling coupe size

Choice of coupe size is based on a compromise between achieving maximum operational efficiency and cost effectiveness (leading to large, regularly shaped coupes) and a desire to ensure that the shape and size are in scale and sympathy with the surrounding landform. The compromise considered acceptable in the Kielder landscape results in felling coupes of 5–20 ha (average 12 ha) in the lower zone, 25–50 ha (average 35 ha) in the middle zone, and 50–100 ha (average 80 ha) in the upper zone.

New compartments

Using the boundary and size criteria outlined above the forest has been divided up into proposed permanent management units (felling coupes). Stock maps at 1:10 000 scale were marked to show roads, watercourses and other natural features such as crags and the new compartment boundaries were drawn along these, a process sometimes labelled re-compartmentation. In some areas where there was a shortage of roads, watercourses or crags it was necessary to use other important and functional features such as public footpaths or (exceptionally) existing rides. A new compartment numbering system was imposed in which the first digit represents the zone (lower, middle or upper) in which the compartment lies and thus it is possible to glean, from its number alone, a picture of the size, location and management prescriptions for a particular compartment.

Age class distribution

Having established the pattern of felling coupes in relation to space it was then necessary to consider the timing of felling. To achieve a meaningful difference in appearance and structure it was considered that adjacent coupes should not be felled within 10

Table 17.4 Time-span available for age class manipulation

Windthrow hazard class	Age at 0.1 m³ average tree	Age at terminal height	Years available
3	32	71	39
4	32	51	25
5	32	47	15
6	32	39	7

years of each other if at all possible and that the objectives should be to achieve, within any currently massive even-aged areas, a justifiable distribution of 10-year age classes. The achievement of this requires felling to take place both before the age of maximum discounted revenue (the optimum financial rotation) and beyond the optimum. In practice, retention of stands beyond the optimum rotation is greatly affected by their expected stability.

Table 17.4 shows, for the average Kielder stand of general Yield Class 12 managed on a no-thin rotation, the ages at which terminal height occurs and the timescale between reaching harvestable size and reaching terminal height. It is clear that a full rotation can only be achieved on sites of windthrow hazard classes 3 and 4 and that the option of retaining stands beyond the optimum rotation only exists on windthrow hazard class 3 sites: clearly then, most of the manipulation of stand age class distribution has to be achieved by premature felling. This is unfortunate because the financial penalties associated with extending the rotation are less than those associated with shortening it by an equivalent number of years due to the latter option significantly reducing the log content of stands. It is also clear that the time available for achieving a diversification of

age classes is very short, particularly in windthrow hazard class 6 areas where, first time round, all that may be achievable is the felling of every other coupe at 0.1 m³ average tree and the remainder 7 years later at terminal height, in order to achieve effectively a two-tier age class matrix. In practice the situation is eased since, in any given area, there is usually enough local variation in species, yield class and topography to enable a reasonable span of felling ages to be achieved. Nevertheless, the difficulties associated with achieving restructuring at the first attempt in areas of high windthrow hazard class, should not be underestimated and the need for careful planning to exploit such opportunities as exist is paramount.

Introduction of broadleaved trees

The introduction of broadleaved tree and shrub species into an otherwise coniferous forest is one of the most positive steps that can be taken to enhance wildlife habitat except where populations of red squirrel need to be preserved. It is essential, however, that such introductions are planned to take account of long-term forest structure, the need for efficient timber harvesting and the need to exploit the most suitable sites for the establishment of broadleaved species. In Kielder, as in many upland forests, it is considered that watercourses form the most suitable foci for such developments for the following reasons:

1. Since watercourses are frequently used as felling coupe boundaries, the location of broadleaved woodland 'corridors' in such areas will provide permanent windfirm edges to the felling coupes as well as ensuring that the corridor need not interfere with or be affected by the felling operations in the adjacent coupes. They must be sited therefore so that they do not isolate the conifer crop from the harvesting roads.

2. Watercourses are natural, linear features providing, in most cases, a ready made framework which is acceptable in landscape terms.

3. The creation of a permanent network of corridors provides extensive opportunities for colonisation and migration of associated wildlife species.

4. Many watercourses have steep sides which, when planted with conifers, present special and costly harvesting problems, often involving the import of skyline winch equipment into an otherwise forwarder based harvesting system.

5. Watercourses tend to be more sheltered and to have better drainage and more fertile soils than adjacent areas and therefore normally provide the most (sometimes only) suitable sites for the planting of broadleaved trees in the uplands.

6. Planting of conifers near to watercourses may have adverse effects on the physical, chemical and biological characteristics of freshwater habitats.

By selecting, from the compartment planning map, the watercourses which were chosen as compartment boundaries, a network of future broadleaved woodland corridors was identified and, by closer inspection, the actual boundaries of the corridors were identified. In most cases these correspond to the break of slope at the edge of the natural stream valley and hence the corridor width varies from several metres to a few hundred metres. In practice a minimum width of 60 m (30 m each side of the stream) has been adopted. In the forest as a whole some 300 km of watercourses have been identified for future development, which at an average width of 100 m represents an area of 3000 ha or 7% of the plantation area. Coupled with a high broadleaved species component in the areas of the forest identified for 'special management' (more intimate and intricate than restructuring) the end result is ex-pected to be a broadleaved woodland component of 10% of the plantation area. Within each 'corridor' a detailed plan is prepared which has the overall objective of creating 50% broadleaved woodland cover and 50% of open land in the form of glades and deer lawns, intimately mixed with the broadleaved woodland. The staggering of felling ages as a result of the restructuring process means that the clearance of the conifer crop and subsequent restocking with broadleaved species in a particular watercourse is a phased affair and two or three decades may be required before the whole corridor is created. One advantage of this however is that the completed 'corridor' will itself contain a variety of age classes, thus adding further diversity to these broadleaved woodland areas.

Species choice is largely restricted to broadleaved trees and shrubs native to the area: alder, birch, oak, ash, willow and rowan with the addition of small proportions (5% each) of sycamore and Scots pine, the intention being to achieve multi-structured stands with a shrub understorey.

Plant spacing is normally 3 m by 3 m (1000 plants per ha) but an established stocking of 500 trees per hectare is accepted in areas where a low density broadleaved tree cover is sought. No timber production is expected from these areas but since the long-term aim is to create permanent features with diverse structure some degree of management is anticipated. Broadleaved plantings next to forest streams should not be continuous but intermittent, providing sun and shade along stream sides.

Unplanted areas

Open space has much value within the forest whether it is used to make the landscape more interesting, to provide structural diversity, to protect interesting features or to provide areas for culling deer. In the typical first rotation forest such open space may have been confined to areas considered unplantable and to the area devoted to roads and rides, the latter normally accounting for around 15% of the land area. The ride system installed at time of planting in Kielder, as in many forests, was based largely on a relatively geometric pattern which did not, other than by chance, relate the open space to any positive feature. The identification of future felling coupes has resulted in new compartments often consisting of several of the old compartments complete with their geometric ride pattern.

When restocking the new compartments no attempt is made to retain the old ride system and only a perimeter ride is left unplanted. This has the effect of reducing the area taken up by roads and rides from 15% to around 8%. To replace some of this open space in a more environmentally constructive way, opportunities are sought at time of restocking to build into the new compartments a proportion of open space using the figure of 5% as a guideline and with the proviso that each unit of space should be at least 0.5 ha so as to be mappable, identifiable and effective. Thus in a 60 ha restock it would be usual to have around 3 ha of open space, perhaps made up of six separate units. Selection of sites for open areas is based on identification of the following features:

1. Sites or archaeological importance.

2. Perennial watercourses which have not been scheduled as broadleaved woodland corridors but which may benefit from having a 20 m clear area on each side. (See *Forests and water guidelines* published by the Forestry Commission.)

3. Interesting botanical features.

4. Areas likely to be useful for future deer management.

   In the ideal situation it is possible to combine one or more of the above elements. An open area around a watercourse, for example, can if carefully shaped also be useful for deer control and deer lawns can often be created around areas left open to protect a site of archaeological interest.

The identification and planning of open space is therefore an important element of restocking planning.

Extended rotations

The retention of a proportion of conifer stands beyond their economic rotation has value in further diversifying the age class structure and in providing additional wildlife habitat associated with large, open structured stands. In wind-prone forests like Kielder the opportunities for such retentions are limited but the identification of stands in areas of local topographic shelter gives some scope for retentions, even if only for 10 years beyond the expected rotation. As with the planning of broadleaved woodland corridors, the siting of such retentions must be such that they do not unduly impede adjacent harvesting operations and, most importantly, that the retained area has easy access to a road so that the eventual clearance of the stand can be carried out without undue difficulty. Retaining stands in the middle of a restocked area leads to future extraction difficulties. In Kielder retained stands are expected to account for only around 1% of the forest area because of the windthrow difficulties.

Effect of forest structure and diversity

The result of following the restructuring principles outlined is the gradual transition from a first generation even-aged plantation with relatively little structural diversity to a more varied forest having a structure which contains numerous elements both static and dynamic. The static elements are represented by the broadleaved woodland corridors, the planned and managed open spaces and the areas identified for long-term retention. All of these features will remain in the same place although their degree of development will change with time.

The dynamic element is represented by the conifer component which will consist of a continuum of stand heights, spatially distributed throughout the area, ensuring that at any one time there will be approximately the same area of each habitat type and all habitat types will be represented in any one sector of the forest.

One of the most important elements of a restructured forest in comparison with a first generation forest is likely to be the amount of edge, defined as a place where distinctly different habitat types meet. Ecologists agree on the special value of edges. Total length of edge in a typical restructured area of Kielder is likely to be around 90 metres per hectare whereas in many of the first generation areas of the forest figures as low as 20 metres per hectare may be encountered. The exact effect on wildlife of the increased structural diversity, of the dynamic nature of some of the components and of the interaction between the different components can only be a matter of supposition until further research is carried out. What is assured however is that total wildlife diversity in a restructured forest will be markedly greater than in either the first generation forest it replaced or on the open hill ecosystem which preceded it.

The current version of restructuring concentrates largely, within the conifer component, on the achievement of between stand diversity by maintaining a matrix of compartments of different crop ages, while within each compartment the emphasis is on a uniform timber producing stand, albeit with some built in open areas. Further opportunity for habitat

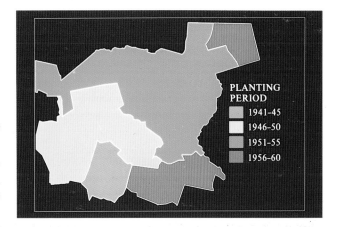

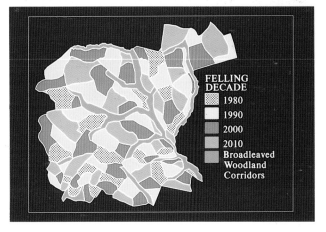

Plans of part of Kielder forest showing the transition from first generation even-aged plantations to a more diverse age structure in the second rotation.

enrichment lies in increasing the within-stand diversity by, for example, the encouragement of a naturally regenerated broadleaf component. In the average fenced Kielder restock area naturally regenerated birch and rowan may occur at a density of 200 plants per hectare and these may provide additional interest without unduly affecting timber yield.

The landscape issue

The need to fell to windfirm boundaries in most of the forest can cause problems in reconciling the restructuring approach with theoretical principles of landscape design. The choice, as compartment boundaries, of natural features such as watercourses, particularly when they are subsequently restocked with broadleaved species, provides the opportunity to achieve acceptable shapes in many cases. Where, however, the result is a compartment shape which is unacceptable in landscape terms, the only solution may be to delay restocking some parts of felled areas for later inclusion in the restocking of the adjoining coupe when it is felled some 10 years later.

Effect on revenue

Since restructuring involves the deliberate felling of stands at other than the optimum economic age, there must be a financial penalty. The cost penalty associated with felling before the optimum rotation age is greater than that incurred by felling an equivalent number of years beyond the optimum (Table 17.5). However, where rotation length is physically limited by windthrow problems, premature felling must be the main means of diversifying the forest age class structure. Hence greater cost penalties are involved in Kielder than would be the case in more windfirm forests. However a comparison between actual and potential revenue must take account of other factors which necessarily reduce financial yield.

Felling coupe and roading rationalisation

To achieve the ideal in which every stand is felled at the age at which discounted revenue is greatest would often involve the construction of expensive roads to harvest small areas of mature timber which

Table 17.5   The financial penalties of felling at other than the optimum age

Age relative to optimum*	Percentage reduction in discounted revenue
−15	−46
−10	−25
− 5	−12
0	0
+ 5	−9
+10	−16
+15	−24

* Defined as the felling age at which discounted revenue is maximised.

reach the optimum age in advance of neighbouring stands. This would be impractical and counterproductive because of the high roading cost. Similarly the felling of such small areas in advance of neighbouring stands would lead to high establishment and protection costs. Thus whatever management system is adopted, rationalisation of felling coupes and roading requirements is likely to be necessary and is likely to lead to a reduction in potential financial yield.

Smoothing of production peaks

Since the original planting of Kielder was subject to irregular land acquisition it follows that any attempt to maximise yield would lead to a broadly similar pattern of felling with large peaks and troughs in production. This would create difficulties for both harvesting resources and marketing strategy benefiting neither the grower nor the user. Smoothing of the peaks and troughs is therefore necessary to achieve a relatively steady increase in production which will tend to flatten out when the sustained

Kielder Forest is becoming one of Britain's most visually attractive upland forests.

yield level is reached. Since windthrow hazard dictates that such smoothing should be done by felling stands early rather than late, this sensible management policy will clearly result in financial penalties, regardless of any restructuring considerations. The latter are largely subsumed in the former.

Price-size considerations

The calculation of age of maximum discounted revenue is based on a long-term view of the relationships between tree size, value and harvesting cost. Short-term fluctuations in the relative value of small and large trees do occur. It is fortunate that much of the recent felling in Kielder has taken place in a period when the price differential between small and large trees has been substantially less than that contained in the current Forestry Commission price–size curves which are based on long-term assumptions. Thus the real financial penalty of early fellings is now significantly less than might normally be the case.

Environmental influences

Felling that simply optimises economic returns would, as already described, lead to large-scale felling coupes with unacceptable effects on landscape, wildlife and recreation aspects. Though not readily quantifiable, such effects have a clear influence on policy and must be balanced against any financial penalties incurred.

The concept of maximising discounted revenue is therefore largely an academic one. In any sizeable forest there are a number of influences which must result in a departure from the economic ideal, regardless of whether or not a restructuring approach is adopted. The extent to which the adoption of restructuring principles leads to additional penalties is hence difficult to isolate and quantify as are the environmental benefits gained from such an approach. Ultimately an evaluation of the acceptability of restructuring depends on a subjective assessment of the relative merits of the environmental benefits gained and the cost penalties incurred.

Conclusions

The design concepts embodied in the Kielder restructuring plan are a reflection both of the physical limitations imposed by windthrow and a desire to achieve what is considered a reasonable balance between timber production and environmental enhancement. Considerable commitment and planning is required to achieve the objectives set and costs will be incurred, but these relate largely to the first rotation. If most of the age class manipulation can be achieved in this period then subsequent fellings can take place at nearer the optimum time without adversely affecting the desired pattern.

Further reading

Recommended reading in non-Forestry Commission literature

A short list of recent major publications relevant to forestry, mainly by accessible British authors.

AARON, J.R. and RICHARDS, E.G. (1990). *British woodland produce*. (224 pp.) Stobart Davies, London.

BLYTH, J., EVANS, J., MUTCH, W.E.S. and SID-WELL, C. (1987). *Farm woodland management*. (189 pp.) Farming Press Ltd., Ipswich.

EVANS, J. (1982). *Plantation forestry in the tropics*. (472 pp.) Clarendon Press, Oxford.

HART, C.E. (1991). *Practical forestry for the agent and surveyor* (3rd edn). Alan Sutton Publishing, Stroud, Glos.

HART, C.E. (1987). *Private woodlands: a guide to British timber prices and forestry costings 1987*. (154 pp.) C.E. Hart, Coleford, Glos.

HINDE, T. (1985). *Forests of Britain*. (296 pp.) Victor Gollancz Ltd., London.

JAMES, N.D.G. (1989). *The forester's companion* (4th edn). (310 pp.) Basil Blackwell, Oxford.

LUCAS, O. (1991). *The design of forest landscapes*. Oxford University Press, Oxford.

WARREN, P. (1990). *Woodland heritage*. (192 pp.) David & Charles, Newton Abbot, Devon/Nature Conservancy Council, Peterborough.

MATTHEWS, J.D. (1989). *Silvicultural systems*. (284 pp.) Clarendon Press, Oxford.

PETERKEN, G.F. (1981). *Woodland conservation and management*. (328 pp.) Chapman & Hall, London.

PHILLIPS, D.H. and BURDEKIN, D.A. (1982). *Diseases of forest and ornamental trees*. (435 pp.) Macmillan Press, London.

PRICE, C. (1989). *The theory and application of forest economics*. (402 pp.) Basil Blackwell, Oxford.

RACKHAM, O. (1980). *Ancient woodland – its history, vegetation and uses in England*. (402 pp.) Edward Arnold, London.

RACKHAM, O. (1990). *Trees and woodland in the British landscape* (revised edn). (234 pp.) J.M. Dent & Sons, London.

SAVILL, P.S. and EVANS, J. (1986). *Plantation silviculture in temperate regions: with special reference to the British Isles*. (246 pp.) Clarendon Press, Oxford.

SPEIGHT, M.R. and WAINHOUSE, D. (1989). *Ecology and management of forest insects*. (374 pp.) Clarendon Press, Oxford.

WATKINS, C. (1990). *Woodland management and conservation*. (160 pp.) David & Charles, Newton Abbot/Nature Conservancy Council, Peterborough.

WESTOBY, J. (1989). *Introduction to world forestry*. (228 pp.) Basil Blackwell, Oxford.

Subject index of Forestry Commission publications

Subject	Bulletins	Handbooks	Field Books	Guidelines	Occasional Papers	Booklets	Forest Records	Leaflets	R&D Papers	Research Information Notes
Forestry in Britain	63, 65, 80, 84, 97, 99	3, 5	3–7, 10		14, 15, 17, 23, 27	15, 20	122	83		
Seed, nursery practice, tree improvement	59, 66, 83				20, 22				139	143, 190
Silviculture, establishment and tending	62, 73, 75, 76, 78, 89, 92, 95, 102	2, 7	8	1	21					164, 195
Diseases and disorders	69, 70, 74, 79, 86, 88, 93, 94, 98, 100, 101		12				126, 129	20, 79	146, 147, 149, 150	
Insects	67, 85	1			19	53			135	128
Wildlife management	71, 81, 90,	4		3	26, 28		123, 124	82, 86	137	126, 165, 180
Fire protection								80		
Wind	87				24, 25			85		
Management for timber production	64, 72, 82		2			39, 48, 49				
Harvesting, forest roads, marketing, utilisation	68, 77, 91, 96		1, 9, 11		29		128	75, 81	144	
Landscape, recreation, planning for the second rotation				2			130			

Availability of FC publications

An annual *Catalogue of publications* is produced by the Forestry Commission and lists those titles currently in print.

Forestry Safety Guides

The Safety Guides published by the Forestry Safety Council give a summary of safe working practices helping employees and employers to comply with the Health and Safety at Work Act 1974. In many cases an appropriate checklist is available for use by supervisors, safety officers, etc., at inspections. All are available free from the Publications Section, Forest Research Station, Alice Holt Lodge, Wrecclesham, Farnham, Surrey, GU10 4LH or from the Forestry Safety Council, 231 Corstorphine Road, Edinburgh, EH12 7AT.

FSC Guide No.	Title	Checklist available
N	Noise and Hearing Conservation	*
1.	Clearing Saw	*
2.	Dipping Plants in Insecticide (and Packing and Transporting)	*
4.	Pre-planting Spraying of Containerised Seedlings	*
5.	Application of Pesticide by Hand Held Applicators	*
6.	Tractor Mounted Weeding Machines	*
7.	Planting (including Plants Treated with Insecticide)	*
8.	Hand Weeding	*
9.	Brashing and Pruning with Handsaw	*
10.	The Chain Saw	*
11.	Felling by Chain Saw	*
12.	Chain Saw Snedding	*
13.	Chain Saw – Crosscutting and Stacking	*
14.	Chain Saw – Take Down of Hung-up Trees	*
15.	Chain Saw – Clearance of Windblow	*
17.	Chain Saw – Felling Large Hardwoods	*
18.	Tree Climbing and Pruning	*
21.	Forest Tractors	*
22.	Extraction by Skidder	*
23.	Extraction by Forwarder	*
24.	Mechanical Harvesting	*
25.	Extraction by Cablecrane	*
26.	Use of Tractors with Winches in Directional Felling and Takedown	*
30.	Mobile Saw Bench	*
31.	Mobile Peeling Machine	*
32.	Fencing	*
33.	Hand Held Power Posthole Borer (Rock Drill)	*
34.	First Aid	*
35.	All-Terrain Cycles	*
	A Joint FSC/Electricity Supply Industry Code of Practice: The Avoidance of Danger from O/H Electric Lines and Underground Electric Cables in Forests and Plantations	

List of addresses

Forestry Commission

Headquarters

The Forestry Commission
231 Corstorphine Road
Edinburgh
EH12 7AT
Tel: 031 334 0303

Research Stations

Forest Research Station
Alice Holt Lodge
Wrecclesham
Farnham
Surrey, GU10 4LH
Tel: 0420 22255

Northern Research Station
Roslin
Midlothian, EH25 9SY
Tel: 031 445 2176

Other useful addresses

Arboricultural Association
Ampfield House
Ampfield
Nr Romsey
Hants
SO51 9PA
Tel: 0794 68717

Association of
   Professional Foresters
Brokerswood House
Brokerswood
Nr Westbury
Wiltshire
BA13 4EH
Tel: 0373 822238

British Timber Merchants'
   Association (England
   & Wales)
Stocking Lane
Hughenden Valley
HIGH WYCOMBE
Bucks
HP14 4ND
Tel: 0240 243091

Countryside Commission
John Dower House
Crescent Place
CHELTENHAM
Gloucestershire
GL50 3RA
Tel: 0242 521381

Countryside Commission
   for Scotland*
Battleby, Redgorton
PERTH, PH1 3EW
Tel: 0738 27921

Countryside Council for
   Wales
Plas Penrhos
Ffordd Penrhos, Bangor
Gwynedd, LL57 2LQ
Tel: 0248 370444

English Nature
Northminster House
PETERBOROUGH
PE1 1UA
Tel: 0733 340345

*From April 1992 the Countryside Commission for Scotland and the Nature Conservancy Council HQ for Scotland will be merged to form Scottish Natural Heritage.

Institute of Chartered
Foresters
22 Walker Street
EDINBURGH
EH3 7HR
Tel: 031 225 2705

Joint Nature Conservation
Committee
Northminster House
PETERBOROUGH
PE1 1UA
Tel: 0733 340345

Nature Conservancy
Council
HQ for Scotland*
12 Hope Terrace
EDINBURGH
EH9 2AS
Tel: 031 447 4784

Royal Forestry Society of
England Wales &
Northern Ireland
102 High Street
TRING
Hertfordshire
HP23 4AH
Tel: 044 282 2028

Royal Scottish Forestry
Society
11 Atholl Crescent
EDINBURGH
EH3 8HE
Tel: 031 229 8851/8180

The Tree Council
35 Belgrave Square
LONDON
SW1X 8NQ
Tel: 071 235 8854

Timber Growers United
Kingdom
Admel House
24 High Street
Wimbledon
LONDON
SW19 5DX
Tel: 081 944 6340

Timber Growers United
Kingdom
5 Dublin Street Lane
South
EDINBURGH
EH1 3PX
Tel: 031 557 0944

TRADA
Stocking Lane
Hughenden Valley
HIGH WYCOMBE
Bucks
HP14 4ND
Tel: 0240 243091

United Kingdom
Softwood
Sawmillers'
Association
16 Gordon Street
GLASGOW
G1 3QE
Tel: 041 221 6551

Woodland Trust
Autumn Park
Dysart Road
GRANTHAM
Lincs
NG31 6LL
Tel: 0476 74297

Addresses of ADAS, DAFS and
WOAD regional offices are given
in the local telephone directory.

*From April 1992 the Countryside Commission for Scotland and the Nature Conservancy Council HQ for Scotland will be merged to
form Scottish Natural Heritage.

Glossary

Apical dominance – Growth concentrated on the leader, which tends to produce a straight stem and conical crown.

Bare root stock – Plants lifted from the nursery soil and despatched to the planting site with their roots bare of soil.

Beating up – The replacement of trees which die or fail to develop after planting.

Billets – Pieces of small diameter round timber cut to length.

Brashing – The removal of lower branches up to a height of about 2 metres to facilitate access for thinning or other purposes.

Cambium – Cellular tissue beneath a tree's bark, in which the annual growth of wood and bark occurs.

Canker – Dead area of a branch or stem caused by fungal or bacterial attack.

Canopy – The mass of foliage and branches formed collectively by the crowns of trees.

Compartments – Permanent management units of land within the forest, divided into stands or sub-compartments.

Coppice – Trees felled close to the ground so as to produce shoots from the resulting stools, giving rise to successive crops of poles and sticks cut over a rotation.

Coupes – Areas of forest which have been clear felled.

Ecotypes – Sub-populations of tree species, with slightly different characteristics, which are suited to a particular environment.

Epicormic branching – A trait of some species to grow small shoots out of otherwise clean stems. Small knots in the sawn timber result.

Flushing – The commencement of growth of a plant above ground, characterised by sap flow and swelling and bursting of buds.

Forwarders – Tractors which extract timber lifted entirely clear of the ground. The timber is carried on a linked trailer or integral rear bunk.

Genotype – The true genetic make-up of a tree.

Girdling – Damage to a tree in which bark has been removed from its entire circumference.

Honeydew – Sticky exudate produced by aphids.

Lop and top – Woody debris from cutting operations, sometimes converted to chippings.

Monocultures – An area of forest in which only one species is present or largely dominates.

Mycelium – The vegetative part of a fungus, consisting of white filamentous tubes.

Needle cast – Defoliation of conifers as a result of disease.

Phenotype – Combination of the genetic make-up of the tree, the environment it is growing in, and the interaction between these two effects.

Pitwood – Wood used in mining.

Racks – Routes created during thinning operations for extracting felled timber.

Roguing – Removal of poor genotypes from an orchard.

Roundwood – Timber in the form of logs or billets.

Sawlogs – Logs, usually of at least 14 cm top diameter, which are intended for conversion in a sawmill.

Scarification – The breaking-up of the ground surface by machine prior to planting.

Skidders – Tractors which extract timber by lifting one end clear of the ground and pulling it out, with the other end dragging on the ground.

Snedding – The removal of branches from a tree.

Standard – Individual tree left to grow on to maturity.

Stands or sub-compartments – Areas of forest comprising a more or less homogeneous crop in terms of age, species composition and condition. Their boundaries may change as the forest develops after felling and restocking.

Treeshelter – Plastic tube placed around a newly planted tree to encourage fast early growth and offer some protection from mammals and chemical sprays.

Undercutting – Severing the roots of small trees in order to improve development without transplanting.

Windfirm – Descriptive of trees and plantations that, because of species, soil or relative exposure, are unlikely to suffer windthrow.

Windthrow – Uprooting or breakage of trees caused by strong winds.

Xylem – Living woody tissue.

Index

(Where headings are followed by a string of references the most important are printed in **bold** type)

Printed in the United Kingdom for HMSO
Dd.0293208   8/91   C100